ELECTRONIC
CRYSTAL SET

by

F. A. WILSON
C.G.I.A., C.Eng., F.I.E.E., F.I.E.R.E., F.B.I.M.

BERNARD BABANI (publishing) LTD
THE GRAMPIANS
SHEPHERDS BUSH ROAD
LONDON W6 7NF
ENGLAND

First Published – May 1982

British Library Cataloguing in Publication Data
Wilson, F. A.
Electronics simplified: crystal set construction.
1. Radio – Receivers and reception – Amateurs' manuals
I. Title
621.3841'366 TK9956

ISBN 0 85934 067 8

Printed and bound in Great Britain by Cox & Wyman Ltd, Reading

PREFACE

This is a book written especially for those who wish to participate in the intricacies of electronics more through practical construction than by theoretical study. Although the reader becomes involved with some of the important fundamental concepts of radio this is through a text which is descriptive rather than mathematical, in fact nothing more than moderately simple arithmetic is used.

Anybody can own a radio set, it just needs money. But not everybody can build even the most modest of sets for it requires both knowledge and skill. This book is designed to help the reader to acquire both and is for all ages upwards from the days when one can read intelligently and handle simple tools. The original crystal set is no longer with us but it has a modern counterpart and the circuits are still the basis of radio receivers so the reader in fact discovers much about the wonders of modern radio, not to any great depth of course but sufficient to make the subject challenging. There is a great sense of achievement when first listening to one's own assembly of bits and pieces, while understanding just a little about how it functions gives confidence when things do not work out as planned for then the fault can be traced without recourse to help from big brother, Dad, or a neighbour.

The book replaces several now out-of-date ones on crystal set construction in the Babani Books series, especially the very successful "Boys' Book of Crystal Sets" by W.J.May. But why should boys have all the fun?, girls and adults are just as capable of building radio sets and enjoying such a fascinating hobby. Nevertheless although suitable for practically everyone the author has the young people in mind, to help the many who have difficulty in choosing a career. It is therefore radio construction with a difference and although it can be considered as a painless introduction to some of the important facets of electronics it is seriously educational with the idea that it may develop an enquiring mind and lead to the young reader finding whether or not the subject is inspiring. Certainly the World is so desperately short of electronics people that choosing such a career is bound to lead to life-long employment in the years ahead when it will be electronic devices themselves which will tend to reduce the availability of jobs.

So many crystal set circuits exist that it is doubtful whether anything novel could be designed hence the ones here are specially chosen from the earlier publications as those from which we can learn most. Also with many books the various coils to be constructed need a very mixed bag of reels of wire, some of which are difficult to obtain, it has therefore been worthwhile to modify the circuits so that fewer different sizes are needed.

Finally the cost of components is small for we do it all as inexpensively as possible.

F. A. Wilson

CONTENTS

CHAPTER 1
SOME IMPORTANT FACTS

t is not difficult to build a crystal receiver successfully, all ne has to do is to follow the instructions given later in the ook but it is far more exciting and rewarding if we under-tand just a little of how it works. Thus in this first chapter ve get started with some radio and electronic principles ut without getting involved in mathematics or complicated heory.

Ve use the metric system throughout and readers who are till uncertain about it will find an ordinary desk ruler marked n centimetres and millimetres of great help.

.1 VIBRATION

et's start with speech and music for these make up most adio programs and let us see how they arise through *vibration*. ll the instruments of an orchestra produce sound by causing omething to vibrate, the strings of a guitar or piano, the archment of a drum, the reed of a saxophone or clarinet, ven the air in a flute. When we ourselves talk, we push air up hrough our vocal cords and these vibrate. We can however ook to the pendulum of a clock for an easily understood xample of vibration, it swings to and fro between two points nd is said to *oscillate*. Vibration is the same type of motion nly much faster and when something vibrates it makes the air round it do the same, creating *sound waves* which reach our ars and we hear sound.

he clock pendulum may swing to and fro once or several imes each second. One complete swing, for example, from eft to right and back again to the left is called a *cycle* and he number of cycles completed in one second is called its *frequency*, in *Hertz* (named after a German physicist and abbreviated to Hz).

Often in electronic engineering we need to draw a *graph* or picture of such a vibration and we can imagine this being done as in Fig.1(i) for the pendulum. With an inked brush fixed as shown and with the paper moving, a wavy line is drawn and if for example the paper moves at 1 centimetre (cm) each second and the pendulum swings at 1 Hz (that is one to and fro movement per second) then the graph drawn on paper would appear as in Fig.1(ii) where the centre line is marked with a time scale.

This last graph is the form which we use to show a vibration pictorially. It is generally called a *frequency*, in this case of 1 Hz.

Audio frequencies (that is, those which can be heard) range upwards from about 20 to 20,000 Hz, from the lowest notes of a piano or organ to the highest as of a piccolo. Something vibrating at twenty thousand times in one second may be difficult to appreciate but it is nothing compared with the frequencies at which electrons can be made to vibrate, a million million times in one second is quite commonplace. So we are going to be confronted with very large numbers which are fortunately simplified by the metric system for just as 1 kilometre is the same as 1000 metres so 1 kilohertz is the same as 1000 Hz and the upper audio frequency of 20,000 Hz becomes 20 kHz. (kilo = 1000).

Now we all know how quickly sound waves are lost as they travel through the atmosphere so radio broadcasting uses much higher frequencies which peculiarly enough are not lost to the same extent. These *radio waves* are made to "carry" the audio frequencies of the program as we shall see later but first we should ourselves get rid of the confusion people experience with radio transmissions labelled both in "frequency" and "wavelength".

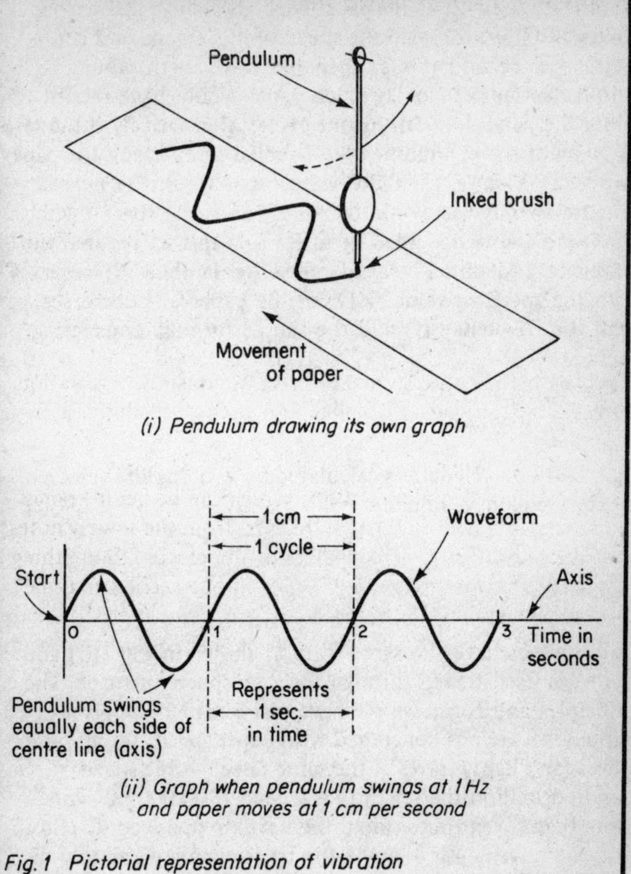

(i) Pendulum drawing its own graph

(ii) Graph when pendulum swings at 1 Hz and paper moves at 1 cm per second

Fig. 1 Pictorial representation of vibration

1.2 FREQUENCY AND WAVELENGTH

The dual labelling arises simply because the swing of the *waveform* of Fig.1(ii) can be described in two different ways, (i) as a frequency of 1 Hz or (ii) as the length along the axis of one cycle which is known appropriately as the wavelength. However the wavelength on the paper depends on how fast the paper moves and if we doubled the speed of movement to 2 centimetres per second (cm/s) then the wavelength would be *doubled* because twice as much paper would have moved under the pendulum during one cycle. Alternatively if the rate of swing of the pendulum were doubled to 2 Hz and the paper moved at 1 cm/s, then the wavelength would be *halved* because two cycles would be packed into the space on the graph previously occupied by one. From this we see that the wavelength (denoted by the Greek letter lambda, λ) increases with the speed or velocity (v) of the paper but decreases with the frequency (f) and the simple formula connecting them is

$$\lambda = \frac{v}{f},$$

that is, the wavelength is calculated by dividing the velocity by the frequency. Equally

$$f = \frac{v}{\lambda}.$$

Radio waves have the same form as shown in Fig.1(ii) and the wave itself travels through the atmosphere or space. The principles and formulae we have just examined apply but happily we are not concerned with paper speeds for all radio waves (and light) travel at the same unbelievable speed, three hundred million metres in one second (300,000,000 m/s – more than seven times round the Earth in one second!) So to find the wavelength of any radio transmission we simply divide 300,000,000 by the frequency (in Hz, not kHz), nasty numbers to deal with so the table in Appendix 1 is added as a guide, it covers the transmissions we will be tuning in on our crystal sets later. These range over the long and medium wavebands as follows:

Long Waves:	1000 – 1875m	(160 – 300 kHz)
Medium Waves:	190 – 550m	(545 – 1580 kHz).

As an example, a station broadcasting on 909 kHz has a wavelength of

$$\frac{v}{f} = \frac{300,000,000}{909,000} = 330 \text{ metres (330m).}$$

As radio constructors we shall often find it more convenient to work in frequency rather than wavelength even though many radio set tuning dials are only marked in the latter.

1.3 ELECTRONS and ELECTRICITY

We all know about *gravity*, something which brings us down to earth with a bump. We attract the Earth according to our size and the Earth attracts us according to its own size and we know which one wins. But we do not know how gravity works, only that it does. It is indeed fortunate that Nature put gravity there or we would disappear into space. It is a powerful but unseen *force*, the strength of which is around us always, we are said to be within its *field.*

These few remarks will perhaps help in appreciating another arrangement of unseen forces due to something we call *charges*. Whereas there is only one gravity which always attracts, there are two different charges which either attract or do exactly the opposite, that is, repel each other and this is according to which of the two types meet. They are labelled positive (+) and negative (–), and there is a simple law which governs their behaviour, "like charges repel, unlike attract".

Electricity is not new, it has been around since the world began. It is the movement of *electrons* which are tiny *negative* charges, within anything, the air if there is a flash of lightning, along mains wires in the home or even through us if we touch something "live". The stuff of which any substance is made (even us) is built up of *atoms*. Each atom has some electrons all to itself just like the Sun has its planets (the Earth is one) revolving round it. An atom with its full complement of electrons is neither positive nor negative because it has a *positively* charged centre which just balances the *negative* charges on its electrons. However some of these little ball-shaped electrons can escape from their parent atoms, a neighbouring positive charge attracts them towards itself or a negative charge pushes them away. When this happens a free electron moves on its own in the spaces between the atoms and because it has lost a negative charge, the atom becomes positive. When electrons are freed in this way and pushed in one direction, this constitutes an *electric current*. This is shown pictorially in Fig.2,

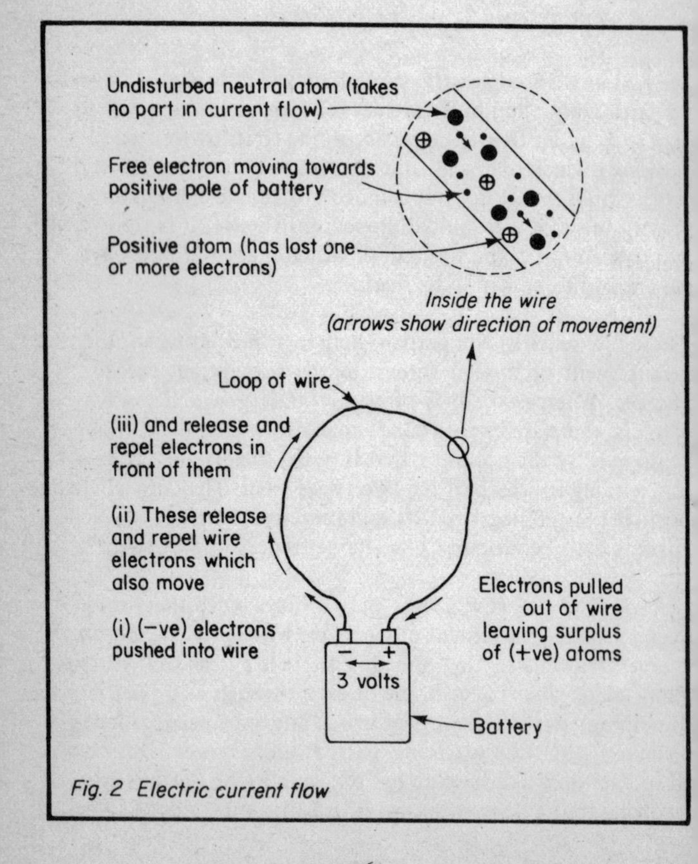

Fig. 2 Electric current flow

where a battery is sending a current round a loop of wire. Chemical action within the battery has the effect of stripping electrons from their atoms and forcing them to crowd at the negative terminal, leaving positive atoms at the positive terminal. The more this happens, the greater the build-up of charge at each terminal and the difference in charge between the two terminals is called the *voltage*, in Fig.2 we have labelled it 3 volts. Thus higher voltage means greater charges which can therefore free and move more electrons in the wire, that is, cause a greater current.

The electron is tiny, so tiny in fact that we get lost in a sea of noughts when considering how many are involved in doing a job. Just as a single example, about 18 million million million (18 followed by 18 noughts) flow through a motor car head-lamp bulb every second to light it. No wonder we can never see them.

So we can sum up by saying that an electron is a small charge of electricity normally living with an atom but when lots of them break away and move together in one direction, an electric current flows. When more exist at one point relative to another there is said to be a voltage between the points.

In Fig.2 the electron current is in one direction only and is known as a *direct current* (d.c.) If the battery connexions could be changed over at some very fast rate, electron flow in the wire would reverse its direction at the same rate, it is then known as an *alternating current* (a.c.) and audio and radio frequencies are such, that is, current flowing one way then the other at some frequency. As mentioned earlier we must get used to the idea that these tiny electrons can change direction millions of times in one second.

1.4 CONDUCTORS and INSULATORS

The fact that atoms give up electrons to make an electric current is the basis of electronic engineering, making currents of some predetermined size flow when and where we want. However not all atoms release electrons freely, in fact those of some materials hang on to them so tightly that releasing an electron is almost impossible. This divides materials broadly into two categories, *conductors* in which the atoms willingly give up electrons so that a current can flow, and *insulators* in which they do not. We therefore use a conductor to carry a current and wrap it with an insulator to stop the current going where it should not.

We rate the *ease* with which a material passes a current as its *conductance* but in practice we usually talk in terms of the opposite, its *resistance* (to current flow). Conductors have a low resistance, insulators high. Resistance is measured in *ohms*, (shorthand Ω, the Greek letter omega), practical values run from fractions of one ohm for a short length of wire to millions of ohms, expressed as megohms (MΩ) for insulators. In between there are kilohms (kΩ, 1kΩ = 1000Ω). Everything has a value of resistance, even we have.

We might see the relationship between voltage, current and resistance by considering a crowd of football fans at the stadium gates. The game is soon to commence and, anxious to get in, they create pressure on the gates. Each fan may be likened to an electron and those at the gates are being pushed by the agitation and anxiety of those behind. The pressure on the gates is the *voltage* but being closed, they present an infinitely high *resistance*. Nobody gets in (zero current). Now if the gates are opened slightly the gate resistance has fallen and some fans enter the ground (lower resistance, increased current). With the gates flung wide open everybody pours in (even lower resistance, high current). It is clear that the number of fans getting into the ground per minute (current) increases both with the pressure built up behind them (the driving force, voltage) and as the gates are opened more (lower resistance).

Copper is a good conductor and is used extensively in electronics for wires and components, silver is slightly better but expensive. For insulators we can use for example, rubber, mica, most plastics, porcelain, glass or air. Thus wires usually consist of a copper conductor either bare or more usually coated with plastic (for example, electric light flex), current flows along the wire and it is confined to it by the insulation. Enamel is also an insulator so for many electronic purposes the insulation on a copper wire may consist of a thin coating of enamel only. This saves space but it must be treated with care for the enamel is easily damaged. In electronics diagrams when a wire is indicated for conducting current from one part or component to another we simply draw a single line and it is understood that the wire is either insulated or if not, supported in such a way that it touches nothing along its length. We will see how wires are drawn on circuit diagrams later.

There are many thicknesses or *gauges* of wire available from the hair-line to pencil thick. The world classifies them in different ways although generally the metric system is taking over in which a wire is described by its diameter in millimetres. Two other systems are still much in use, the *Standard Wire Gauge* (SWG) and the *American Wire Gauge* (AWG). Naturally we will use metric but where appropriate the nearest other gauges are also quoted.

Semiconductors are materials used in transistors etc. and they are neither good conductors nor good insulators, somewhere about half-way (semi = half).

1.5 RESONANCE

The pendulum mentioned in Section 1.1 is capabl f keeping a clock accurate because it has a *natural* perio oscillation which depends only on its length (the short he pendulum, the faster it goes). It does not matter ho rd it is pushed, eventually a pendulum settles down same time per cycle. A piano or any other music ng similarly has a natural period of oscillation bu higher frequency, for example, for middle C the string vibrates at 262 Hz. The frequency in this case is determined by the thickness of the string and the tension in it and the piano tuner simply adjusts the tension to get the note right. When the note is played the wire is struck and set in vibration but it vibrates only at 262 Hz and this is called the *resonant* frequency. Similarly for all the other piano notes each wire has its resonant frequency. Resonance is a feature of all musical instruments by which they generate the delightful sounds we hear.

An electrical circuit can also resonate, that is, respond to one frequency only and two special components are required, an *inductor* and a *capacitor*. The inductor is a coil of wire and it has a distinctive property of *reactance* which affects a.c. only. The capacitor is a very different component from the inductor, it comprises metal plates which can hold a charge, it too has the property of reactance. We will not go into detail about these components yet because we will be looking at them more closely later. What is important here is that the inductor has one type of reactance which we label positive and the capacitor has the opposite type, so it is labelled negative. As with charges, a positive reactance can be cancelled out by an equal amount of negative reactance. The reactance of an inductor *increases* as frequency goes up but that of a capacitor falls and

> at low frequencies the reactance of an inductor is low, that of a capacitor is high
>
> at high frequencies the reactance of an inductor is high, that of a capacitor is low

so as frequency rises from low to high, with the reactance of the indu tor rising and that of the capacitor falling, at some value they re both the same and cancel out.

Reactance, eit positive or negative, is rather like resistance, it tries to stop cu t flowing so a circuit containing the two components can pa high current at the frequency at which the reactances cance a lower current at all frequencies above and below this because the reactances do not cancel, there being more positive than negative or the other way round. The two components constitute a resonant or *tuned* circuit and we can begin to see how a radio receiver separates the wanted radio frequency from the others.

Let us now put this on a *circuit diagram* as in Fig.3. In diagrams the symbols are as shown and the shorthand for an inductor is L and for a capacitor, C. In Fig. 3(i) because both L and C have fixed values the circuit resonates at one frequency only. To make it resonate over a *range* of frequencies, for example the long or medium wavebands, we could vary either L or C and it will soon be evident that to vary C is much easier so Fig.3(ii) shows the complete tuned circuit we will construct. Variable capacitors are only available with certain maximum values so the inductors are wound to suit.

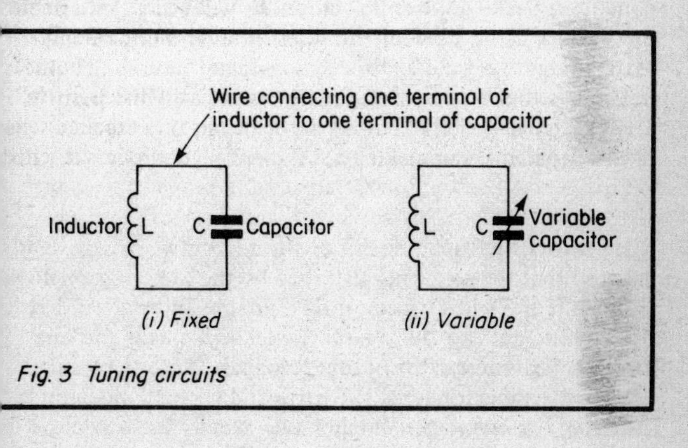

Fig. 3 Tuning circuits

1.6 AERIAL and EARTH

The drawing of Fig.3(ii) is therefore that of a tuned circuit capable of selecting one radio frequency out of the many offered to it. The radio waves are collected and delivered to this circuit by an *aerial* (also known as an *antenna*). Away at the radio transmitter we might imagine that the transmitting aerial is shaking a charge of electrons to and fro as we might shake a rope to make it take up a waveshape as in Fig.1(ii). This projects an alternating field outwards and just like the field of gravity, invisible but always there waiting to move anything it can, the radio field or wave causes the electrons in an aerial conductor to flow one way or the other according to the direction of the field at that instant. Technically we say that the field *induces* a voltage in the conductor. The degree to which the electrons flow depends on the strength of the field, the height of the aerial and how good a conductor it is.

Thus we erect an aerial which is simply a long copper conductor suitably insulated where necessary to prevent electrons leaking away. Because we are using no transistors to boost the aerial signals, as large a signal as possible must be collected and for this the earth itself is helpful as a return conductor back to the radio station. It may be surprising that the earth can be used in this way because some earthly materials such as sand and rock are actually insulators but it is obvious that there are countless other paths through the earth each carrying its share of the electrons of a current. One of our problems is in making a sufficiently good contact with "earth".

Fig.4 shows the tuned circuit connected between aerial and earth so that the electrons disturbed by the radio signals flow through it and when capacitor C is suitably adjusted so that the circuit tunes to the wanted frequency, this is the one which appears across the output terminals. Note the symbols used in diagrams for aerial and earth and how a connexion is indicated. A *connexion* implies two metals in such close contact that electrons flow unimpeded from one to the other, the metals are then said to be "in contact".

1.7 MODULATION

We have seen that a radio program consists of audio frequencies of a few kilohertz, yet the radio transmission is at

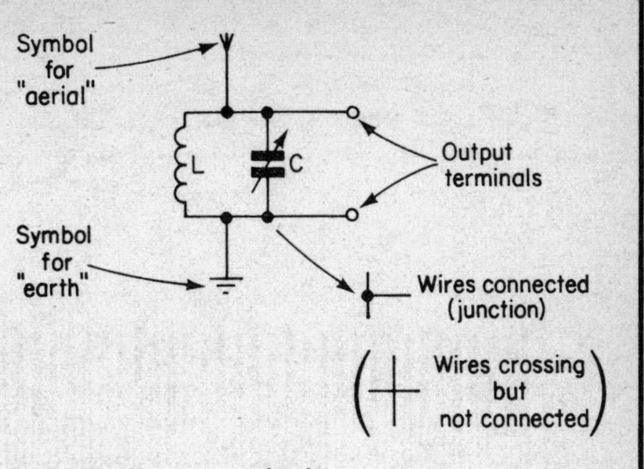

Fig. 4 Aerial feeding a tuned circuit

much higher frequency, up to and over 1000 kHz. The radio requency is called a *carrier* because in effect this is what it loes, it carries the audio frequency on its back, so to speak. The process of getting it to do this is known as *modulation* nd what happens is that the strength or *amplitude* of the adio-frequency (r.f.) carrier is caused to vary according to the mplitude of the audio frequency. This becomes more evident vhen shown pictorially as in Fig.5. The three parts of the igure are all graphs, on a basis of time, of how the amplitude of the modulating (audio), carrier and modulated waves vary. An *oscilloscope*, which is a measuring instrument with a small elevision-type screen, is the electronic counterpart of our ather crude method of making an oscillating device draw its own graph as in Fig.1(i) and this is how Fig.5 would be produced when the appropriate waves are applied to the input erminals. We take a practical example, that of the highest note of the piano (about 4 kHz) being transmitted on a carrier of 200 kHz (1500m) and consider a time period of one thousandth of a second (1/1000s), seemingly a very short time ndeed but in which there are 200 complete cycles of the carrier wave.

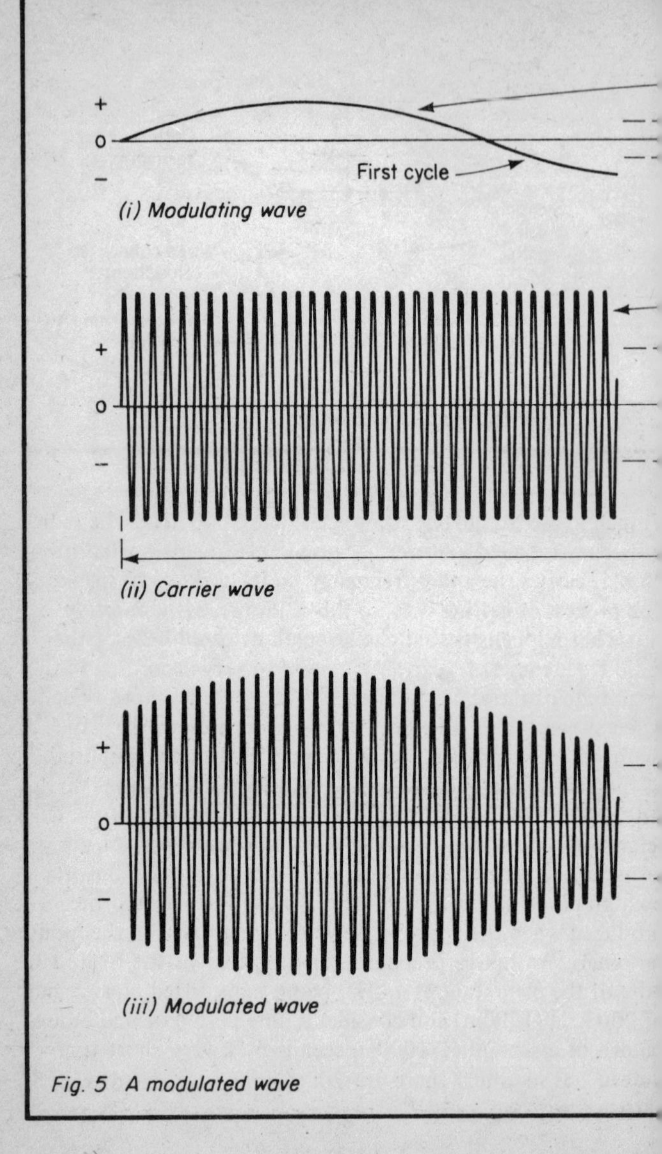

Fig. 5 A modulated wave

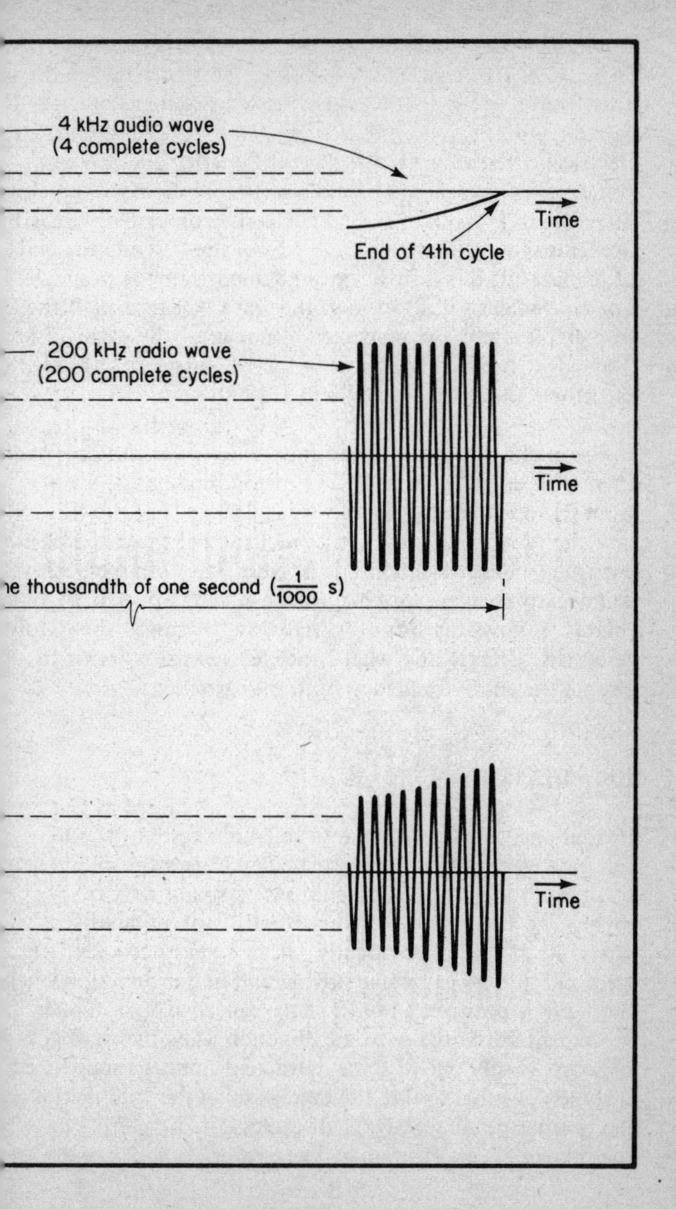
4 kHz audio wave
(4 complete cycles)
Time
End of 4th cycle
200 kHz radio wave
(200 complete cycles)
Time
ne thousandth of one second ($\frac{1}{1000}$ s)
Time

A *microphone* listens to the sound waves generated by the piano wire. Its *diaphragm* vibrates at the frequency of the sound wave hitting it and causes electrons to move in alternate directions in the circuit connected to it. The result is an electrical signal which is a replica of the original piano wire vibration. In one second the audio wave completes 4000 cycles, therefore in 1/1000s exactly 4 cycles are completed. Fig.5(i) does not show all 4 cycles, only part of the first and the end of the last but this is sufficient to demonstrate the principle. For convenience it also shows the wave "cleaned up", the true graph is more complicated although of the same basic frequency. In Fig.5(ii) is shown the r.f. carrier at 200 kHz therefore 200 complete cycles in 1/1000s.

In the modulation process the amplitude of the carrier is made to vary in accordance with that of the modulating wave so from (i) and (ii) in the figure we can deduce (iii), and this is how the program is carried, the frequency of the carrier is not changed whereas its amplitude is. Note that both the positive and negative halves of each cycle are equally affected. Fig.5(ii therefore shows the sort of waveform appearing at the output terminals of Fig.4 and what is needed next is a device to extract the audio frequency from the carrier.

1.8 DETECTION

Headphones work in reverse to microphones, an incoming electrical variation at audio frequency causes the diaphragm to vibrate accordingly and hence set up sound waves in the ea canal. The form shown in Fig.5(iii) is not suitable for operating headphones directly because the movement of electrons in the headphone driving unit in one direction when the wave is positive is immediately cancelled by a similar movement but in the opposite direction when the wave goes negative. Firstly one of these movements must be suppressed, it is then possible to find the average of all the unidirectional (all positive or all negative) half-cycles left. This brings us to the subject of rectification and a *rectifier* or *diode* is a device

/hich allows electrons to flow through it in one direction nly, that is, it can behave either as a conductor or insulator ccording to which of its two terminals is presented with lectrons. Hence if the wave of Fig.5(iii) is applied to a diode ither all the positive half-cycles or the negative ones are locked according to which way round it is connected. Effect-/ely therefore in our example there would be 200,000 uni-irectional *pulses* of current each second. But these pulses re not all equal in strength, they vary in amplitude according o the modulating frequency so by adding them together and omehow finding the average value as we go, the original nodulating frequency is restored. A capacitor is suitable for his because it can store electrons on its plates and so add the arious pulses together. Looking at Fig.5 again the *detection* rocess firstly removes either the top or bottom half of (iii), hen by an averaging process regains (i). We can now complete ur basic crystal receiver circuit diagram as in Fig.6. D is the iode and C_2 the capacitor just mentioned and except for the atter which we will find we can manage without, this is the ircuit we will first build for experience.

ll very well, but we are building a *crystal* set, where is the rystal? This in fact has gone out of fashion and its place is ow taken by the diode, cheaper, smaller, more reliable and

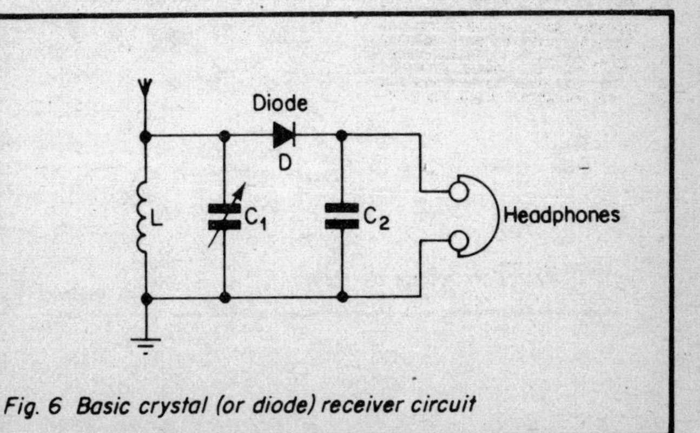

Fig. 6 Basic crystal (or diode) receiver circuit

needing no adjustment. Detection was accomplished in early receivers by means of a contact made between a fine-pointed wire and a crystal of galena, molybdenite or carborundum, each had its particular qualities. To obtain a suitable crystal/metal junction it was necessary to search around the crystal for a responsive spot using the end of the wire until the headphones sprang to life. This could take several minutes so woe to any member of the family thereafter causing sufficient rumpus for the contact to be lost. The wire became known as the *cat's whisker* and just to see what we have missed, Fig.7 shows a sketch of a crystal detector (minus its glass case) with a modern diode for comparison.

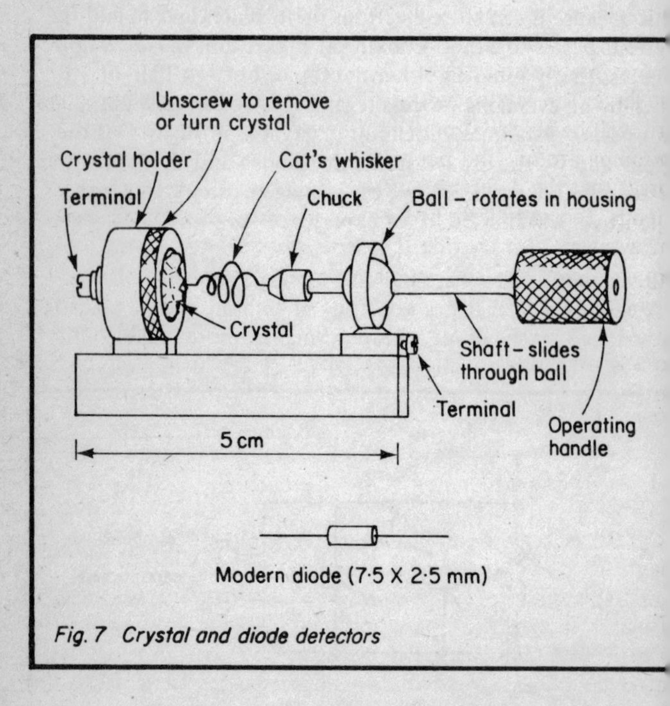

Fig. 7 Crystal and diode detectors

CHAPTER 2
COMPONENTS

ig.6 shows the various components required for a basic ;ceiver. Apart from the aerial and earth there is an inductor _), variable capacitor (C_1), fixed capacitor (C_2), diode (D) ıd headphones. The inductor we will make ourselves .though it could be bought (more of this later), the other ɔmponents can be purchased from a radio component shop r mail-order service. The names and addresses are to be found ı popular electronic or radio constructors' magazines, usually ublished monthly. Catalogues are so large nowadays that a ıarge may be made but to have one is an asset and note that ıe larger the catalogue, the more likely it is that the particular rm will be able to supply all the items required, this saves ıopping around and postage. Nevertheless we must never ɔrget that the defective radio set discarded by the family or iends, too expensive to repair yet somehow too good to ırow away, can provide the experimenter with a plentiful ıpply of useful parts, especially the variable capacitor which e next consider.

o that we understand the components a little better, some otes follow.

.1 CAPACITORS

o the newcomer a capacitor is a mysterious piece of equip- ıent. It has no through connexion as do most other ɔmponents, there is actually an insulator between its two sets f plates. Imagine two plates of metal placed close together ; in Fig.8 and connected to a battery. As seen in Fig.2, a attery is a device which has a high pressure of electrons at s negative terminal and an equal lack of them at the positive ;rminal. When a battery is connected to the plates therefore ıere is a rush of electrons into the l.h. plate and equally out

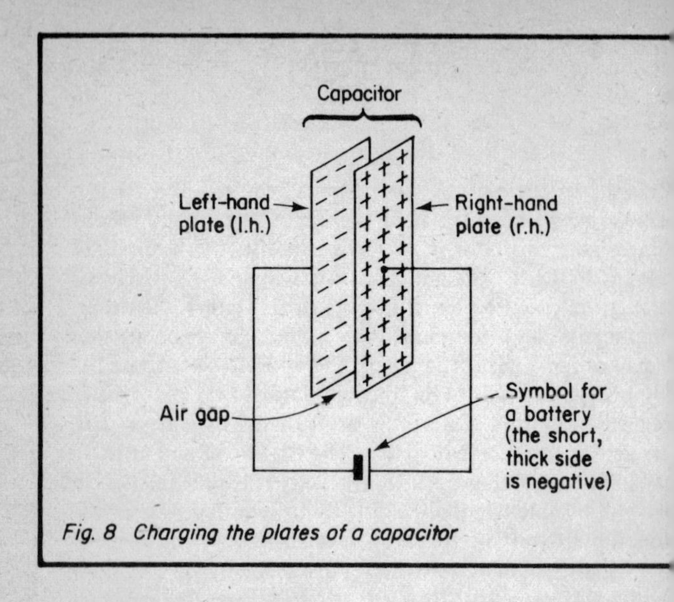

Fig. 8 Charging the plates of a capacitor

of the r.h. plate, in the latter case attracted by the surplus of positive atoms at the battery + terminal. The l.h. plate is therefore negatively charged and the r.h. positive, all in a very short time. There is no flow of electrons across the air-gap between the plates because air is an insulator so the flow ends when, for example, the l.h. plate has reached the same "electron pressure" as that at the battery negative terminal for then there are two equal negative charges opposing each other. The plates are now said to be *charged* and if the battery is disconnected they remain so. If subsequently a circuit or wire is connected across the plates then for the tiniest fraction of a second they act as a battery and drive electrons round until they are *discharged*.

Little imagination is required to see that *capacitance*, which is the capability of storing a charge, depends on the area of the plates. It also varies with the separation between them, reduced separation giving greater capacitance. The insulation between the plates (the *dielectric*) need not be air, other sulating materials are used and the capacitance increased. ne unit of capacitance is the *Farad* but generally in radio e work in *microfarads* (μF – μ is the Greek "mew") which e millionths of a farad or in *picofarads* (pF) each of which is ne millionth of a microfarad. Just to add to our confusion me capacitors are now so small that there is no room to int the value in pF on them so the *nanofarad* is used which is ne thousandth of 1 μF or equally one thousand pF, thus:

nF x 1000 = pF μF x 1000 = nF μF x 1,000,000 = pF

) a 0.0005μF capacitor could equally be quoted as).0005 x 1000)nF, i.e. 0.5nF or (0.0005 x 1,000,000)pF, e. 500pF.

required, C_2 in Fig.6 would be a *fixed* capacitor, with one alue of capacitance only, say about 1000pF (or 1nF). By sing thin dielectrics and plates, such a capacitor is no more an a bead a few mm across in the middle of its two con- ecting wires.

ariable capacitors such as C_1 are more complicated because ey are mechanically operated. Those for tuning radio ceivers have maximum values ranging from about 300 to 00pF. The capacitor works by enmeshing a set of movable lates (many small ones are connected together as the equi- alent of a single large plate) with a second set of plates which e fixed as shown in Fig.9. The dielectric is usually air but olid dielectric types are also available which are more ompact. A (tuning) knob is fixed to the shaft, by turning ockwise the moving plates interleave more with the fixed nes, so increasing the capacity. The moving plates are in ontact with the frame and are therefore connected to the *rthy* side of the tuned circuit. The fixed plates are insulated om the frame.

an old radio receiver is being *cannibalized* (dismantled to rovide spare parts), the variable capacitor is easily recognized. s spindle will be coupled to the tuning dial and it will look something like Fig.9 but duplicated or triplicated, that is two or three complete capacitors on one spindle. This is quite usable, we need only connect one section and improved designs shown later in the book need two sections anyway.

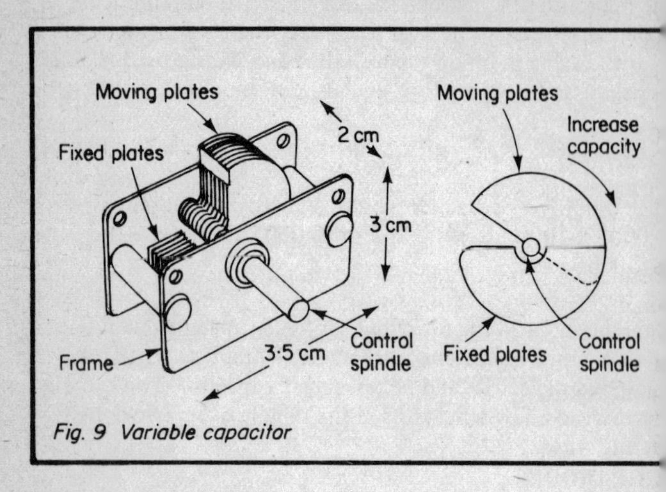

Fig. 9 Variable capacitor

2.2 INDUCTORS

These take many forms but at this stage we consider the *air-cored* type only. Ours will consist of enamelled wire close-wound on a cardboard or plastic tube, the number of turns of the wire being chosen to produce the correct *inductance*. This is measured in henrys, again a large unit for radio constructors so we work in *microhenrys* (μH) one of these being one millionth of 1 henry.

When electrons flow in one direction in a coil of wire, they create a magnetic field running through the centre which can turn a compass needle just as the Earth's magnetic field or that of a permanent magnet does. Again the field is invisible but the force it can exert is there just the same. If the electrons reverse direction, so does the field and if it attracted ne end of a compass needle in the first instance, it would now epel it. Of equal importance is the fact that when the current eases, support for the magnetic field is removed and it ollapses but in so doing, itself creates electron flow in the vindings. In a resonant circuit the rise and fall of the magnetic ield of the inductor is complementary to the discharging and harging of the capacitor. There is a to and fro movement of lectrons between them which is greatest at the resonant requency.

'o cover the medium waveband (Section 1.2) an inductor of bout 200μH is needed.

Enamelled wire is obtainable in over 60 different sizes, a good ne to start with is 0.56mm diameter. Constructional details f coils follow in Chapter 4. Note that the general term "coil" s frequently used instead of "inductor" in radio tuning pplications.

.3 DIODES

tudy of the diode, so called because it has two *electrodes* di = 2) brings us into touch with the semiconductors on which nodern transistor technology is based. Our explanation must f necessity be very simplified and it starts with the two undamental types of semiconductor materials. These are *ilicon* compounds which either have an excess of positive toms or of negative electrons. The first is obtained by mixing ilicon (a grey, brittle material) with a substance which 'steals" electrons from some of the normally neutral atoms hereby leaving them positive, the final material is described s *p-type*. Alternatively a substance can be added which gives xtra electrons to the silicon which is then classed as *n-type*. It s when p-type silicon is placed in contact with n-type silicon hat a diode with its rectifying properties is formed. Fig.10 hows a battery connected across a diode with its junction etween the two semiconductors shown diagrammatically, t of course does not have clean boundary lines as suggested.

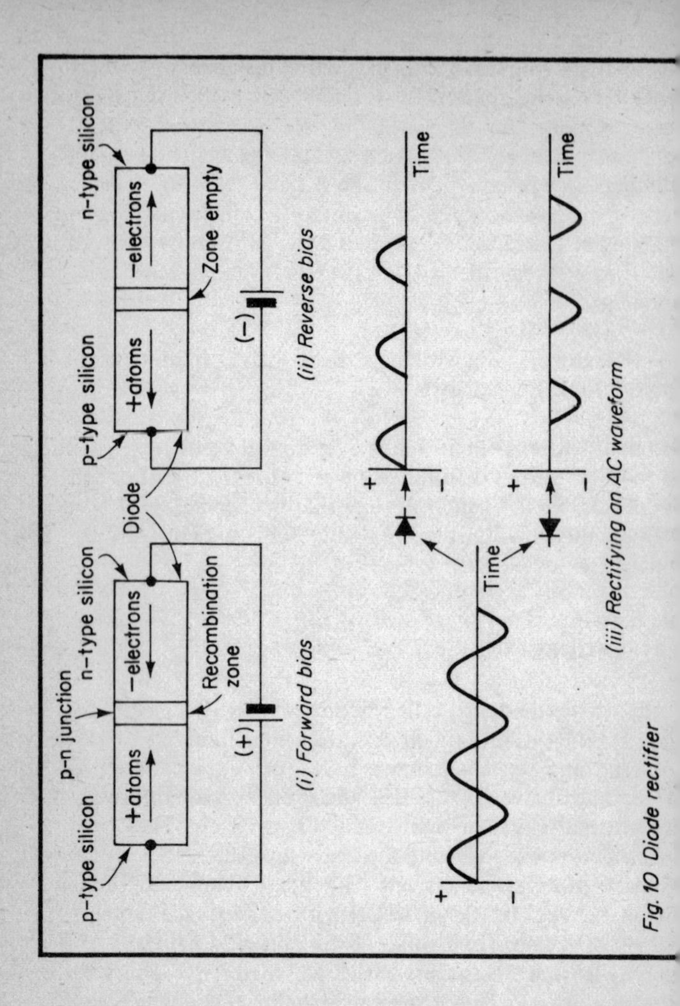

Fig. 10 Diode rectifier

In (i) the +atoms in the p-type and the −electrons in the n-type are forced straight across the junction by the similar charges of the battery. Some recombine to form neutral atoms in the junction area but the battery supplies plenty to make up for this. Thus current flows and the battery is then said to be connected in the *forward* direction.

i) When the battery connexions are reversed as shown, the *urrent carriers* (+ atoms and – electrons) are swept out of ie junction whereupon no current can flow, that is, the evice effectively becomes an insulator. This is the *reverse* irection.

ccordingly, if the battery potential is replaced by an a.c. aveform which in fact swings in both forward and reverse rections, the result is as shown in Fig.10(iii) where one half f each complete cycle is cut off.

'e will see from the diode itself just how tiny the actual inction must be so if too many current carriers are pushed rough the junction at once by applying too high a voltage, ie heat created will burn it out. There are no such difficulties ith a crystal set however because the voltages picked up by ie aerial are minute. But we could be in trouble when oldering a diode wires onto tags because heat from the oldering iron travels along the wires to the junction, a golden ile therefore is not to cut the wires, to solder right at the nds and if possible use a *heat shunt* (see Appendix 3).

.4 HEADPHONES

esistance is mentioned in Section 1.4 and a crystal receiver eeds headphones of 2000Ω resistance or more for most fficient working. Such headphones can be purchased but it is ir better to make use of a type which is more available gen-rally. Nowadays an increasing number of homes possess a air of good quality stereo headphones, usually supplied with i-fi systems, music centres, electronic organs and the like. his naturally saves purchasing them but if they do have to be ought, the low *impedance* types have many more uses for ther projects. We can adapt them for ours.

/e seem to have switched from the term "resistance" to impedance", there is in fact a technical difference between ie two even though they are both quoted in ohms, nevertheless as far as headphones are concerned we can look at both terms as meaning the same.

Stereo headphones are usually connected as shown in Fig.11 to a 6.5mm (¼ inch) jack plug. The wiring arranges for two separate *channels*, one to each earpiece. One wire is common both so only three wires are needed. The plug has *tip*, *ring* an *sleeve* connexions insulated from each other as shown and we need to make our connexions to tip and ring only for the signal current then flows through the two earphones in *series* (that is, one after the other). This also happens to double the net headphone impedance to 16Ω since two 8Ω earphones in series gives 16Ω as shown in Fig.11. However we should nc put 16Ω headphones directly on a circuit requiring a high impedance for some of the signal is wasted in so doing. What necessary is to *match* the headphones to the receiver circuit by making them behave as though they have high impedance and this is effected by a *matching transformer*, miniature one which are used between some transistor circuits and loud-speakers are suitable and inexpensive.

When electrons flow in a winding a magnetic field is set up and if another separate winding is within this field its electron experience a force trying to move them. With a circuit connecting the two ends of the winding they can and do mov and as we say, a current flows. This only happens while the current in the first winding is changing but this is the condition throughout crystal sets because all currents are alternating. A *transformer* consists of two or more separate windings which are in magnetic contact with each other, that is, they are close enough for the magnetic field of one to affect the other. Sometimes, as in the case of matching trans-formers, one winding is wound round the other with both on a metal core, alternatively as we shall find later (Section 5.5) many r.f. transformers have the two windings completely separated. The symbol for a transformer is shown in Fig.11.

Matching transformers convert impedances from one value to another and are sold quoting the impedances between

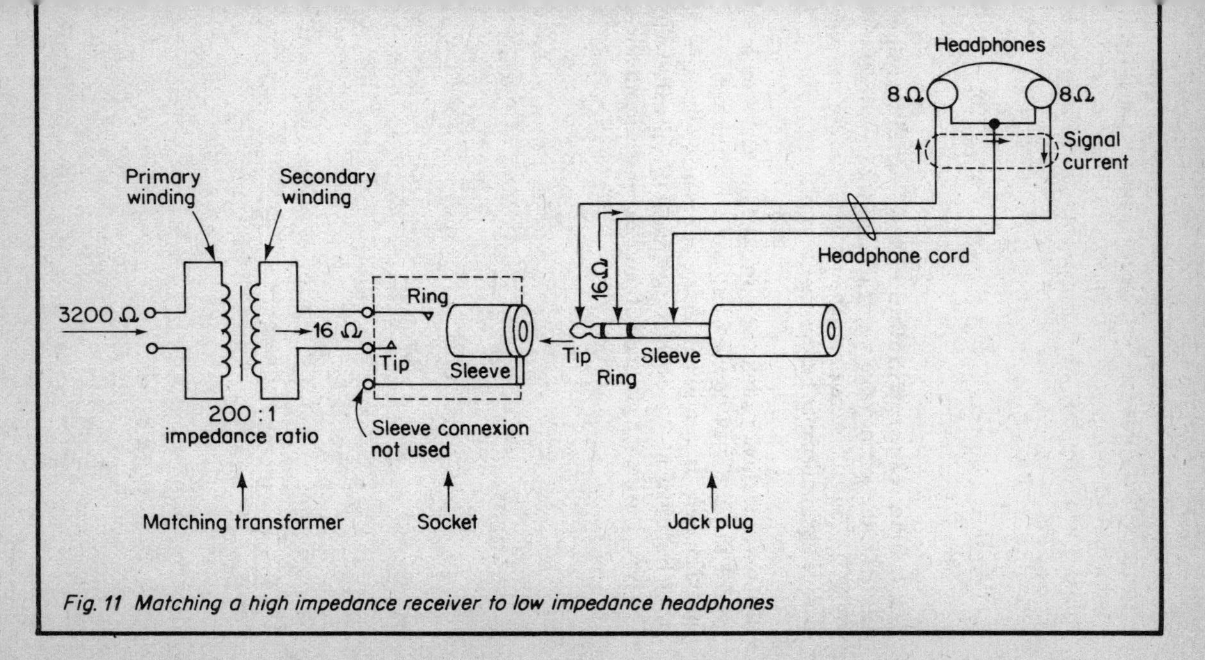

Fig. 11 Matching a high impedance receiver to low impedance headphones

which they should be used. We need not worry if we cannot get exact values as long as the impedance *ratio* is about right. Thus a transformer quoted as *primary* 1.0kΩ, *secondary* 5Ω (primary and secondary are the names of the windings) has a ratio of

$$\frac{1000\Omega}{5\Omega} = 200.$$

This ratio therefore raises 16Ω to 16 x 200 = 3200Ω as shown in Fig.11, the sort of value we are looking for (say, 1500 – 4000Ω). Thus the stereo headphones with transformer can replace high impedance headphones.

If stereo headphones cannot be borrowed, for real economy a crystal earpiece may be used instead, it has the right impedance and is surprisingly cheap, but as might be expected much less efficient. Nevertheless one might usefully start with this type, leaving the purchase of more expensive headphones until later.

CHAPTER 3
AERIAL and EARTH

: is perhaps the two items at the input and output of the rystal set which affect the overall results most, the aerial/ arth system and the headphones. In this chapter we discuss ıe former and how to install it, remembering that we are btaining all the power for driving the headphones from the ıdio wave itself. We must therefore aim for the most efficient ystem possible but one which also suits our particular circum- tances or location. The use of tiny aerials such as are found in ortable receivers can only come by using circuits which are ed with extra power from batteries.

'or our purpose aerial installations can be divided into three lasses, in order of merit they are (i) outdoor, (ii) indoor loft nd (iii) indoor room and the first decision must be as to vhether we are building circuits simply for experience in the rocess of learning or whether a receiver is to be retained for se permanently. This naturally affects the types of wire used nd the effort put into the installation, for example for a emporary installation a length of insulated wire slung around he room may be sufficient but we must bear in mind its mitations. Firstly two important reminders:

i) recalling Section 1.6, the radio signal picked up by the aerial must flow through the tuned circuit, all of it. This implies that there should be no *leakage* paths to earth anywhere along the aerial for if there are, some signal electrons will be bypassed through these paths and be wasted.

ii) the aerial should be as high as possible.

.1 OUTDOOR AERIALS

Jndoubtedly the best type although the most difficult to

provide. Point (i) above reminds us that the aerial must be we insulated from earth all along its length. Air is an insulator so where an aerial runs through open space it can be of bare copper wire but insulated at its two supports. It so happens however that bare wire particularly suitable for outdoor aerials, for example 7 strand, of about 0.72mm (SWG 22, AWG 21 – stranding improves flexibility) may be difficult to obtain except from specialist wire firms so we will think in terms of insulated wire. This also happens to be easier to lead into the house and several kinds are available in most catalogues. Even twin-core plastic-coated mains flex or bell wire can be used quite cheaply as long as the wire itself is not likely to fracture under the tension of a long span. A typical outdoor installation is shown in Fig.12(i). With a little ingenuity and care that pipes or gutters are not pulled off the wall, fixings on both house and distant pole, tree or building can be made. Terminating the aerial wire on its insulators by twisting a loop round the span wire as shown in (ii) of the figure may be difficult with springy plastic-coated wires and here a binding of adhesive tape will help. A temporary insulated wire aerial needs no insulators and the wire can simply be tied at both ends.

The lead into the house must be insulated so if the aerial wire is bare an insulated lead must be jointed to it, preferably by soldering (see Appendix 3). Sometimes a ventilator or ill-fitting window or door will allow a thin plastic-insulated wire to be brought in without drilling through the woodwork (double-glazing makes life really difficult!), so much depends on the house or shed or wherever the receiver is to be used.

3.2 LOFT AERIALS

These are similar to the outdoor type but suspended within a loft or attic. Similar principles apply but in this case the dowr lead is already in the house and may be brought down throug the trap door or a tiny hole in the ceiling. Alternatively it may be run through the eaves and down the outside wall to be led as for the down-lead of an outdoor aerial. Preferably it ould not be cabled down the wall but spaced from it.

3 ROOM AERIALS

ost likely to be used owing to their simplicity, these are ıfortunately the least efficient. Nevertheless many readers ill prefer to forego the rigours of outdoor or loft aerials d use this type. An insulated wire is simply run round the alls of the room (preferably an upstairs one) at picture rail ceiling height back to the starting point at which the down-ad is taken. The wire is fixed by adhesive tape or preferably n through insulated screw hooks to keep it a short distance om the wall. The general arrangement is shown in Fig.12(iii).

4 EARTH

good connexion to earth is essential and is most easily complished via a cold-water pipe (not gas, some of the joints ay not conduct well) and a check should be made that the pe does actually disappear into the ground and not find its ay upwards to a plastic cold water tank in the attic. The pipe ust be scraped or sandpapered clean and a connexion made it by use of a special *earth clip* which is most likely to be ailable from an electrical (mains wiring) supplier. Alter-atively a good connexion can be obtained by wrapping the rth wire round the pipe several times and then tightly visting the free end over the main lead as shown in Fig.12(iv). or added security the loops of wire round the pipe may be ressed more tightly into contact by enclosing within a hose-ip of suitable dimensions. Soldering is preferable but not sily carried out because firstly the pipe must be emptied of ater and secondly a very large iron or gas torch would be quired to heat the mass of metal sufficiently for solder to ow.

ıstead of a water-pipe connexion, a home-made earth spike

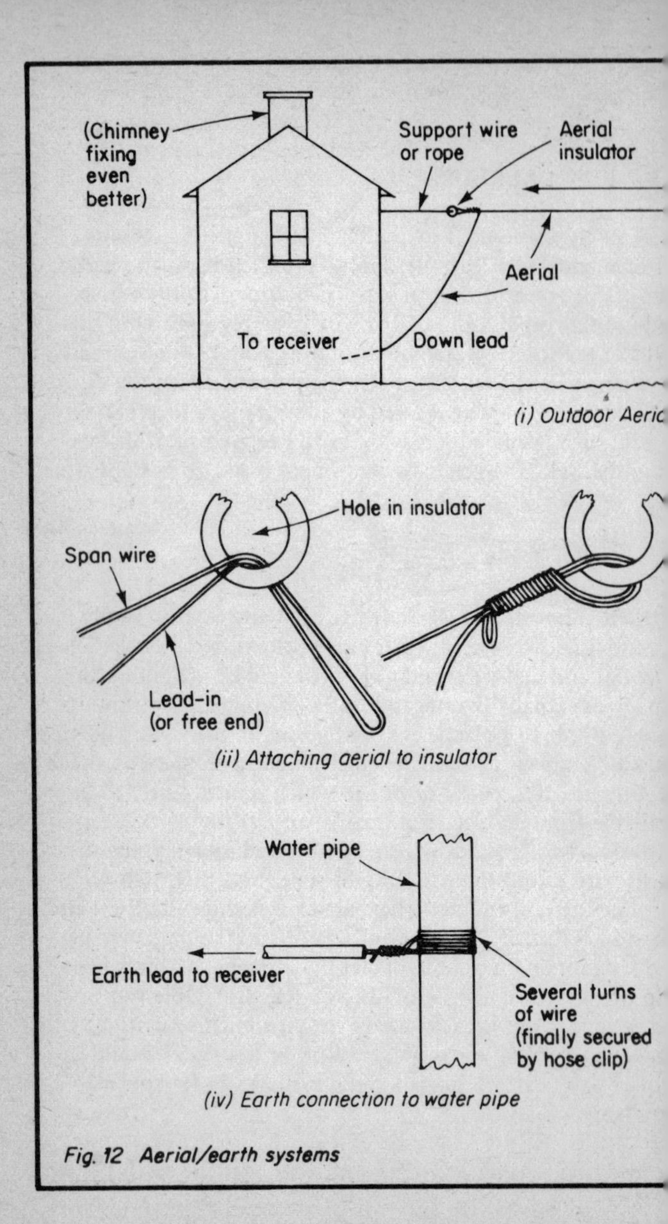
(Chimney fixing even better)
Support wire or rope
Aerial insulator
Aerial
To receiver
Down lead
(i) Outdoor Aeric
Hole in insulator
Span wire
Lead-in (or free end)
(ii) Attaching aerial to insulator
Water pipe
Earth lead to receiver
Several turns of wire (finally secured by hose clip)
(iv) Earth connection to water pipe

Fig. 12 Aerial/earth systems

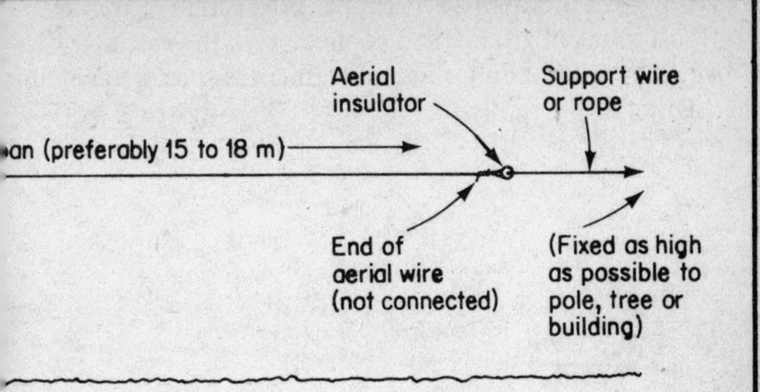

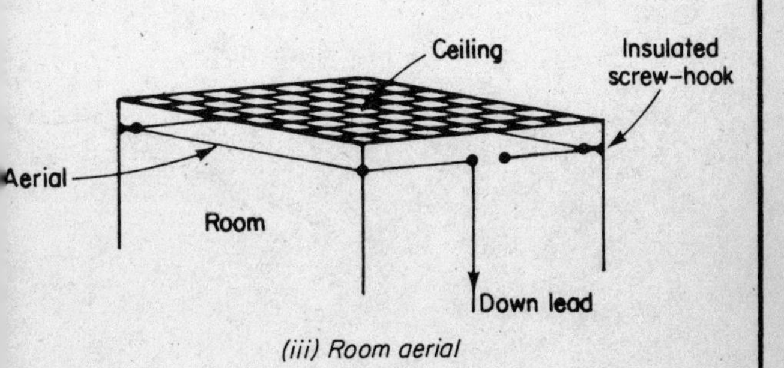

(iii) Room aerial

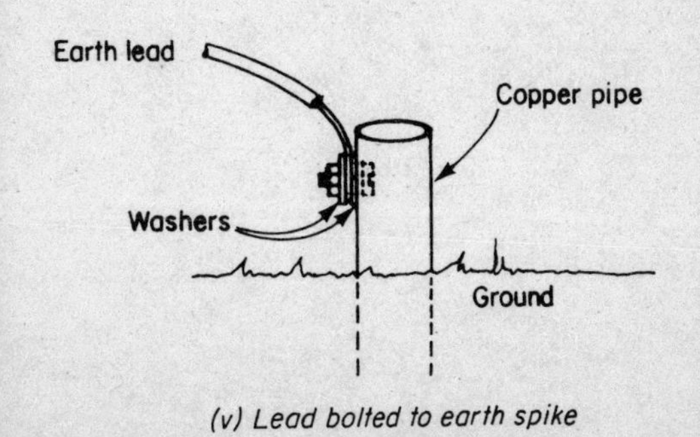

(v) Lead bolted to earth spike

consisting of a metre or so of copper pipe can be driven into previously soaked ground and connected to the earth wire as above or by using a bolt, nut and washers as shown in (v) of the Figure.

CHAPTER 4
BUILDING AN ELEMENTARY RECEIVER

There is nothing to stop us building an advanced receiver first, for example, one of the circuits following later. But since our aim is not only to build sets but also to have at least a little understanding of them it is more sensible to start with the simplest. This will give us practice in wiring and even more important, produce something against which improved models can be assessed. Thus assuming that we now have an aerial and earth at our disposal and are capable of soldering (Appendix 3), we build the circuit of Fig.13(i) which is in fact that of Fig.6 minus C_2 and with the aerial connected just over half-way down the inductor. C_2 may be omitted because the inertia (inability to move quickly) of the headphone diaphragm does the job as well. Each r.f. pulse (as in, say, the top half of Fig.5(iii) will tend to move the diaphragm and it will be helped by those which follow since they arrive in rapid succession. The diaphragm cannot move quickly enough to restore between successive pulses although it is able to follow the slower variations in pulse strength, the audio signal.

This is to be a medium wave receiver and for this, using a variable tuning capacitor of about the average value of those available, i.e. 365pF, the inductor has a value of 230μH so our list of parts is:

- L Air-cored inductor, 230μH (details follow). Requires 18 grammes (just over ½oz) of 0.56mm (SWG 24, AWG 23) enamelled copper wire.
- C Variable capacitor, up to 500pF (see Section 2.1 – for this experimental receiver lower maximum values are in order).
- D Signal diode, AA119, OA91 or equivalent.
- H *Either* crystal earpiece and appropriate chassis or line socket (most likely 3.5mm)

or Pair of 8ohm stereo headphones with appropriate stereo chassis or line socket [most likely 6.5mm (¼inch)] .

T Miniature audio output transformer (see Section 2.4 and Fig.11).

Also: tuning knob, connexion or tag strip, "hook-up" wire.

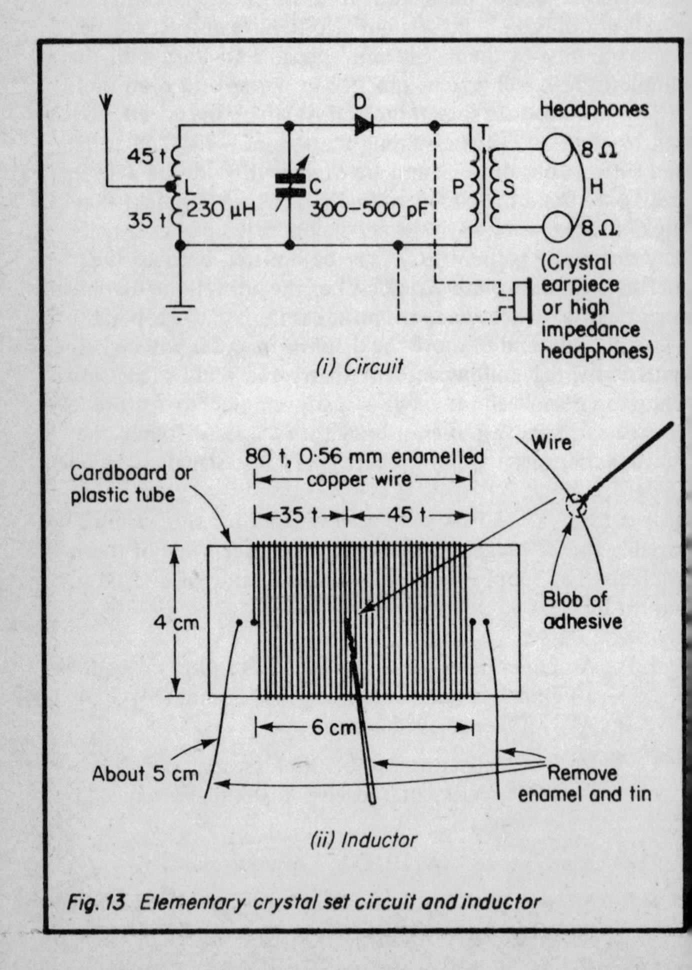

Fig. 13 Elementary crystal set circuit and inductor

4.1 COMPONENTS

For the inductor a small quantity of enamelled wire, say 50-60 grammes (2oz) can usually be purchased, this is ample. 80 turns are wound on a 4cm (1½inch) diameter cardboard tube, we should not need to make one because they abound in plenty as the centre tubes of toilet or kitchen paper rolls. Failing this, any cylindrical plastic container having approximately this diameter and a length of at least 8cm will be suitable. Fig.13(ii) shows details of the inductor construction. Near one end of the tube two small holes about 1cm apart are made for anchoring the wire (a little clear adhesive helps) and some 5cm of wire is left for terminating. 35 turns are carefully wound along the tube, each turn just touching the previous one. Remember the enamel insulation is thin and easily scratched off. At this point a *tapping* is made as shown and again a little blob of adhesive holds the wire. The remaining 45 turns are then wound on, terminating through two holes as before. Scraping off the enamel and tinning the ends of the terminating wires and tapping loop completes the inductor. Should the end turns tend to loosen and ride along the tube, hold in position by pushing a pin through the tube while some adhesive over the wire and tube sets. We shall find after having built this set that modifications to improve it need additional tappings on the same type of coil. Readers who feel competent to tackle the hazards of seven tappings on one winding may prefer to wind the improved coil instead, simply leaving the tappings not required at this stage unused. See Section 5.1 and Fig.16. Precision is hardly needed so wires of diameter within about 10% of 0.56mm (1 gauge SWG or AWG either way) are quite suitable.

The capacitor is discussed in Section 2.1. If one can be obtained from an old radio set, so much the better. We need only a single-gang for this experimental model but some later ones will require 2-gang, leave unused gangs unconnected and check that no moving vane touches a fixed one. If a capacitor has to be purchased it will probably be found that the solid dielectric type is cheaper. Do not be too concerned about the maximum value, Section 5.3 shows that the coil can be adjusted to suit if required.

The tuning knob can be of any type, a large one (4-5cm diameter) makes fine tuning a little easier.

4.2 CONSTRUCTION

The component lay-out and wiring can to a great extent be to individual choice so what follows is one suggestion only, any other arrangement is equally suitable as long as the connexions are the same, that is, Fig.13(i) is followed. In true *breadboard* fashion a piece of wood at least 15 x 11 cm forms the base as shown in Fig.14, its thickness being such as to accommodate the screws holding the capacitor bracket and the terminal block. It is most likely that the capacitor bracket will have to be made, alternatively a small piece of plywood or hardboard nailed or screwed to the edge of the board and drilled for the capacitor to be fitted will suffice. As a general aid in connecting components together a 6-way mains terminal block is shown, these are usually purchased in 12-way flexible units which can be cut down as required. If desired a *tag-strip* may be used instead, all connexions on it being soldered instead of being held by screws. "Hook-up" wire can be purchased but it is possible to make do with many other types such as bare tinned copper, spare enamel-covered or even pieces of single core mains flex or bell wire, ends tinned where necessary. Remember to refer to Appendix 3 if there are still problems with soldering.

Fig.13(i) shows two alternative output arrangements, the crystal earpiece may be used in preference in which case the wires going to the primary winding of the audio output transformer are connected directly to terminals 4 and 5 of the terminal block instead, the transformer being omitted. The diode can be connected either way round, it does not matter whether we end up with the top or bottom half of Fig.5(iii), the result is the same. The miniature audio output transformer will probably fit in as shown, the tags of the secondary winding being connected directly into the terminal block. It is the secondary winding which is connected to the headphones, this is the winding marked with the lower impedance of the two to be matched. A centre tap on the primary is left unconnected.

Should a chassis rather than a line socket be required for plugging in headphones or a crystal earpiece, the appropriate chassis-type socket may be fitted on the baseboard or front panel.

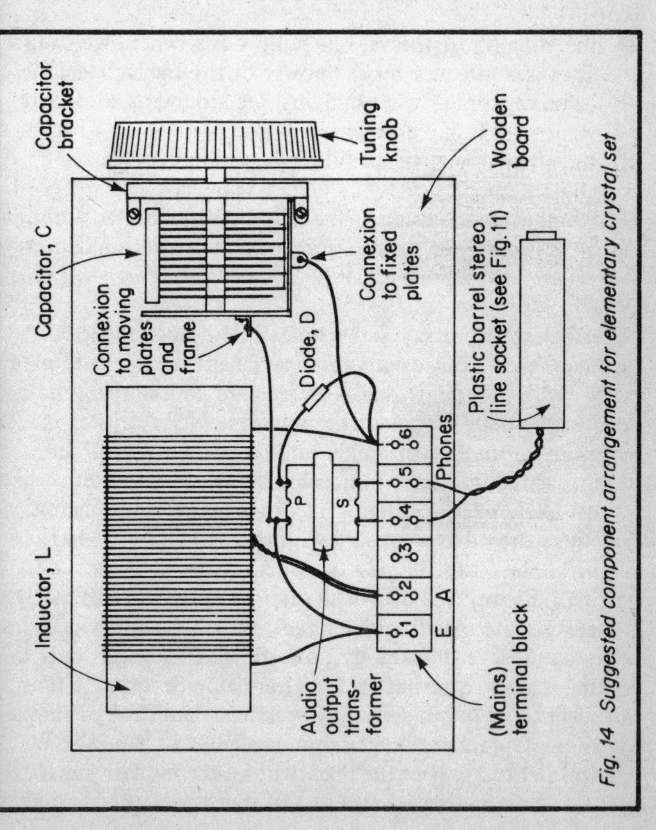

Fig. 14 Suggested component arrangement for elementary crystal set

A few hours work and our first set is completed. We cannot switch on because no on/off switch is required, all the power is free from the air so there is never a need to switch off.

4.3 LISTENING IN

When all is connected as in Fig.14 and with aerial and earth, medium wave radio stations should be heard and now we can assess what we have done. So far it is evident that individual circumstances will differ widely in

(i) the strength of the various radio waves where we live. They are affected by the power of the transmitter, the distance from it, what buildings are around us, and even whether it is day or night,
(ii) the efficiency of the aerial/earth system we have constructed,
(iii) whether we are using high quality headphones or simply an inexpensive crystal earpiece which apart from its lower efficiency uses one ear only.

Nevertheless given, say some moderately powerful local station(s) even a downstairs room aerial and a good waterpipe earth, radio programs should be received with ample loudness on the better types of headphones, with a crystal earpiece not so loudly yet ample on local stations. With an outdoor aerial things are noticeably better all round. But what is most likely to be much in evidence is that radio programs are not separated as we would wish them to be for when the tuning knob is turned a powerful local station may even be heard all the way and drown all others. One of our difficulties is that with the growth of local radio over the last few decades, many of us have moderately powerful radio stations only a few miles away. So what we have learned in Section 1.5 does not seem to work out so well in practice – but this is a simple experimental receiver, many improvements can be made. We have no right to expect the selectivity of the modern superheterodyne receiver with its hosts of transistors, tuned circuits and special techniques. Nevertheless, by starting this way we have gained experience and confidence and will have little trouble in understanding each of the modifications which follow especially if we take them one at a time.

CHAPTER 5
MORE ADVANCED RECEIVERS

Such an uncomplicated receiver as we have constructed cannot be expected to perform as well as a more intricate one so we next look at some refinements, especially those from which can be discovered more about the basic principles of radio.

Readers with no local radio stations may find signals rather weak yet easy to separate while on the other hand those with one or two local stations will probably have more than adequate volume but little choice of station, the local ones swamping everything else and perhaps each other.

Selectivity is the ability of a receiver to respond to a particular radio frequency without interference from others and this may certainly seem to be lacking. However Fig.3(ii) in Section 1.5 considers only the ideal case, that of *pure* inductance and capacitance, that is, no electrons getting lost from the LC circuit in the process. When this does happen then the sharpness of tuning diminishes and the circuit is said to be *damped* – rather like reducing the brilliance of tone of a piano wire by holding a felt pad on it.

The damping arises from other circuits linked with the tuned circuit, in this case the aerial and earth, detector (diode) and headphones. The aerial/earth system hardly looks like a capacitor as in Fig.8, but in fact it is, the aerial wire is one plate, the earth the other. Thus the purity of the inductor is spoilt by having a tiny capacitor (C_a) connected across is as in Fig.15(i). The detector and headphones are connected directly across the tuned circuit and create even more damping, in a simple way we might consider that some electrons flow out of the tuned circuit instead of helping to build up the peak of activity which is required. Effectively this is rather like connecting a resistance (R) as also shown in Fig.15(i).

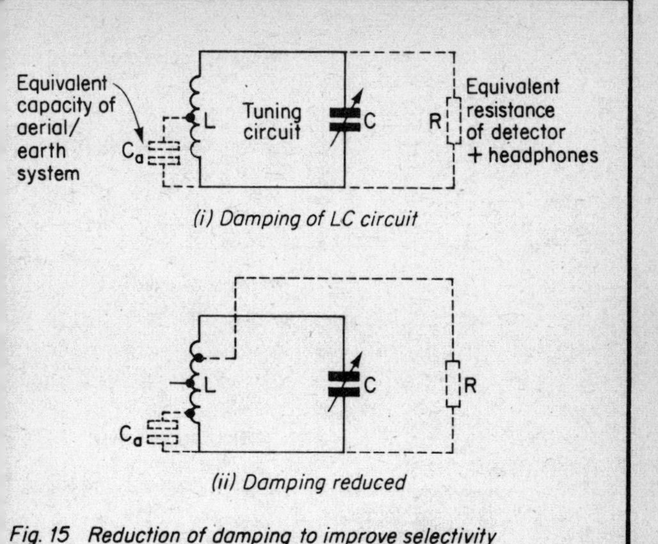

Fig. 15 Reduction of damping to improve selectivity

ne way of reducing the damping with consequent improve-
ent in selectivity is by tapping the aerial and/or diode
wer down the inductor (i.e. towards the earthy end) so that
ey are effective over less turns but therefore unfortunately
oviding a weaker headphone signal. Thus the sharper the
ning, the lower the loudness and obviously we will have to
nd the best compromise between the two.

1 IMPROVING SELECTIVITY

ig.16(i) shows the modified circuit for finding the best com-
omise between selectivity and loudness for each of our own
rticular circumstances. To avoid the possibility of mistakes
hen wiring, a reminder has been added about how wires are
own connected or not connected together on a diagram. The
ductor now has 7 taps instead of one but still has a total of
) turns. There is a tap at every 5 turns from the earthy end

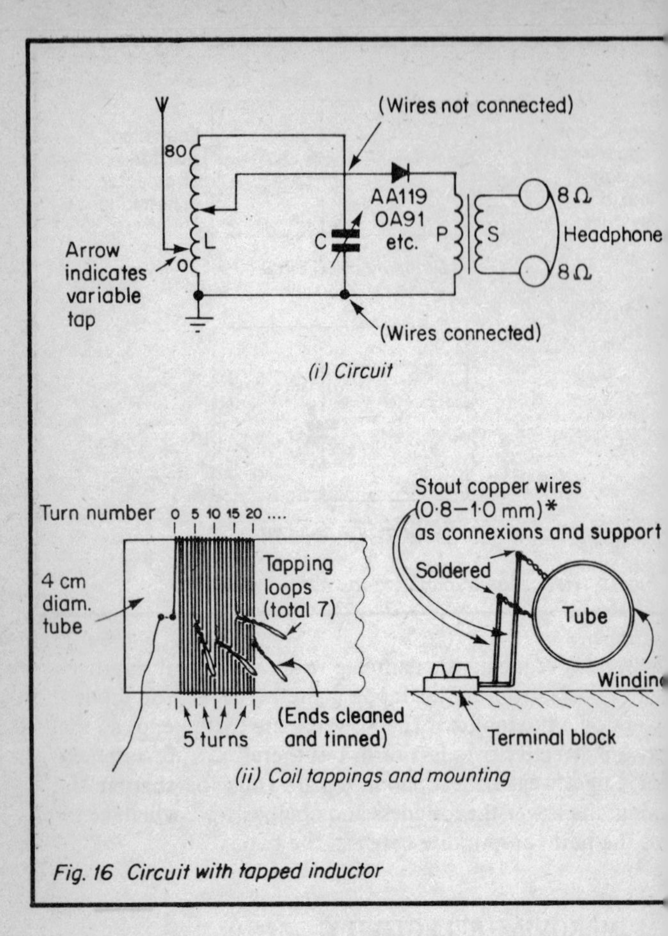

Fig. 16 Circuit with tapped inductor

for the first 35 turns, i.e. 7 taps in all. We can either use the earlier method of a long (5 cm) loop twisted where it leaves the winding or perhaps a shorter loop onto which another wire is soldered. One suggestion is to have loops about 1.5cm long, staggered along the inductor with the latter supported on a 12-way terminal block using stout tinned copper wire supports as shown in Fig.16(ii). Do not be too concerned about support wire gauge, many junk boxes can produce

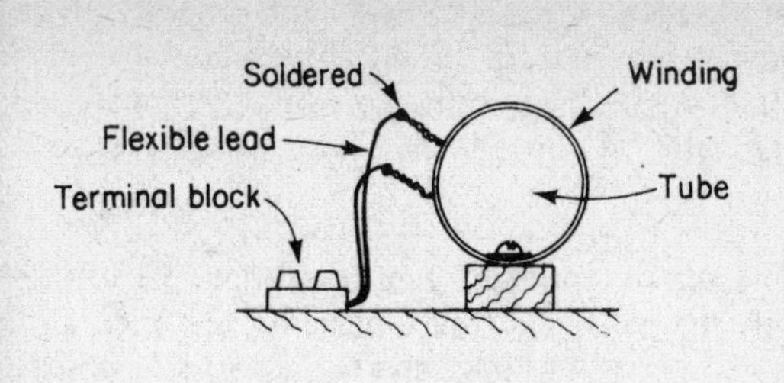

(iii) Alternative mounting

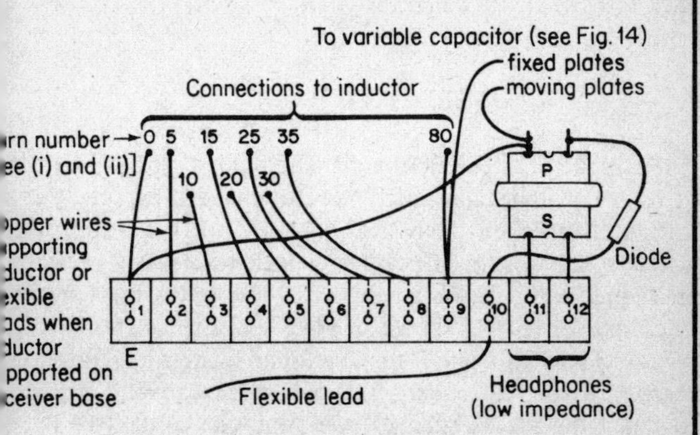

(iv) Suggested component arrangement

21–19 SWG, 20–18 AWG

omething suitable, even the individual strands of scrap pieces f household mains cable. Equally the inductor might be fixed n two small blocks of wood with screws or adhesive as shown Fig.16(iii) with flexible leads to the terminal block or to a g strip instead.

he inductor requires 9 terminals of the block, the remaining conveniently accommodate the headphone transformer (if required) and a *flying lead* for the diode, these components are shown in Fig.16(iv). This is doing the job properly, there i no reason however (except for unreliability of contact) why both aerial and diode flying leads should not terminate on *crocodile clips* and be clipped onto the chosen taps as required.

Earth is connected to terminal 1 and the headphones to 11 and 12. Both the aerial and the diode lead are tried at terminals 2 – 9, a game of "poke and hope" but one which can be rewarding. Remember that generally but not always, the tappings with the lower numbers reduce loudness but increase selectivity. Aerial to terminal 8, diode to 9 brings us back to Fig.13(i) of course.

5.2 SWITCHED SELECTIVITY

A technique of selection of aerial and diode tappings by mear of rotary switches has much to recommend it especially if setting changes are likely to be needed for reception of different stations. In this case two single-pole 8-way switches are required, usually obtainable as 12-way so leaving 4 spare. The drawing symbol shown in Fig.17 speaks for itself with regard to its action and it may be found from catalogues that there are two types of *action*, by which is meant the manner in which the switch changes over from one contact to the adjoining one. *Break before make* switches disconnect one circuit before the next is connected and *make before break* have a change-over period during which both circuits are connected at once for a short time. Either type is suitable for us. A knob to rotate each switch is also required, a small one, say 2 cm diameter or less is ample, if with an indicator line or pointer, so much the better. The modifications to Fig.16 for switching are given in Fig.17.

With such rotary switches a search for the optimum arrangement is quickly made. To tidy up such a receiver a front pane of plywood might be made and drilled to accommodate the

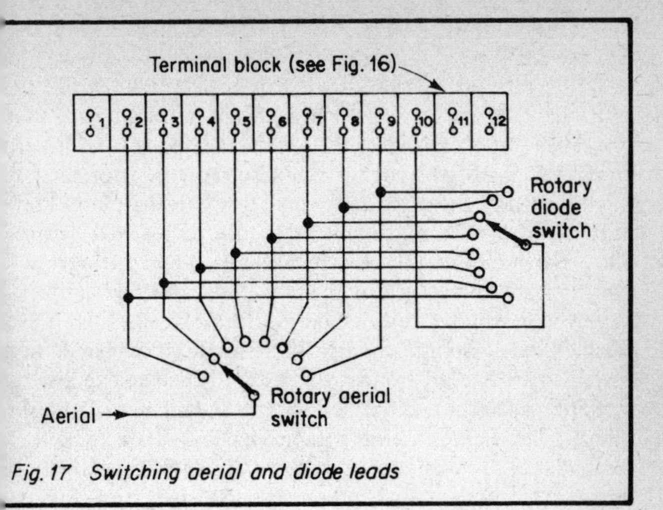

Fig. 17 Switching aerial and diode leads

ıriable capacitor, the two switches and the headphone socket, ıe latter must then be of the chassis type. A pair of terminals ır aerial and earth completes the receiver. On the panel the ıo rotary switches are easily labelled 1 – 8 but we are still ıcertain about a tuning dial because we may not have the ght variable capacitor for the inductor, this is the subject f the next section.

3 GETTING THE RANGE RIGHT

his is where we pause in receiver construction to remove ıme of the confusion which may still exist with regard to ıe tuning ingredients, wavelength, frequency, inductance ıd capacity, each of which has some bearing on the others, ı fit together these four pieces of the puzzle, so to speak. or most crystal sets the inductance is fixed according to ıe variable capacitor available and we tune the receiver over ıe range by rotating the variable capacitor knob over half a rcle. This is normally divided up into 180 *degrees* (180°) shown on any *protractor* and as a reminder as the inner row of figures in Fig.18. The problem is to ascertain where on the dial a particular radio station should be found. Firstly we must relate degrees of rotation of the capacitor spindle with the actual capacitance and we might be forgiven for guessing that for, say, a 365pF capacitor the capacitance value at 0° is zero at at 180° is 365pF, but we could be sadly in error for (i) there is always some *residual* capacity when the plates are fully open, (ii) the maximum value may be reached before 180°. Having found the capacitance at each dial setting and knowing the inductance of the coil, the frequency and/or wavelength can be calculated. For those readers with calculators and an interest in arithmetic, this is explained more in Appendix 2. Fig.18 shows the result of such an exercise for a 365pF capacitor and our coil with its inductance of about 230μH. The figures are very approximate and are for one particular type of variable capacitor only. Most capacitors are designed to conform to a certain specified characteristic but there are inevitable differences in manufacture, furthermore there is no guarantee that our coils have exactly the inductance required. Accordingly it might pay to put on a few more turns than stated and then if wanted stations seem to be missing at the high-frequency end of the range, take some off to lower the inductance and hence increase the resonant frequency.

There is also the problem of having a capacitor of some other value than that used for Fig.18 or perhaps one has been taken from a derelict receiver with no idea whatsoever of the value. Measurement of capacitance is certainly beyond us at this stage, hence the technique above of adjusting the number of turns on the coil is the only one.

As an example of coil adjustment when the capacitance is known, say, 500pF, reduce the coil turns on Fig.13 to 65 – 7 to give an inductance of about 170μH. But if we are happy with a few local stations and none is too close to an end of the band, there is no problem.

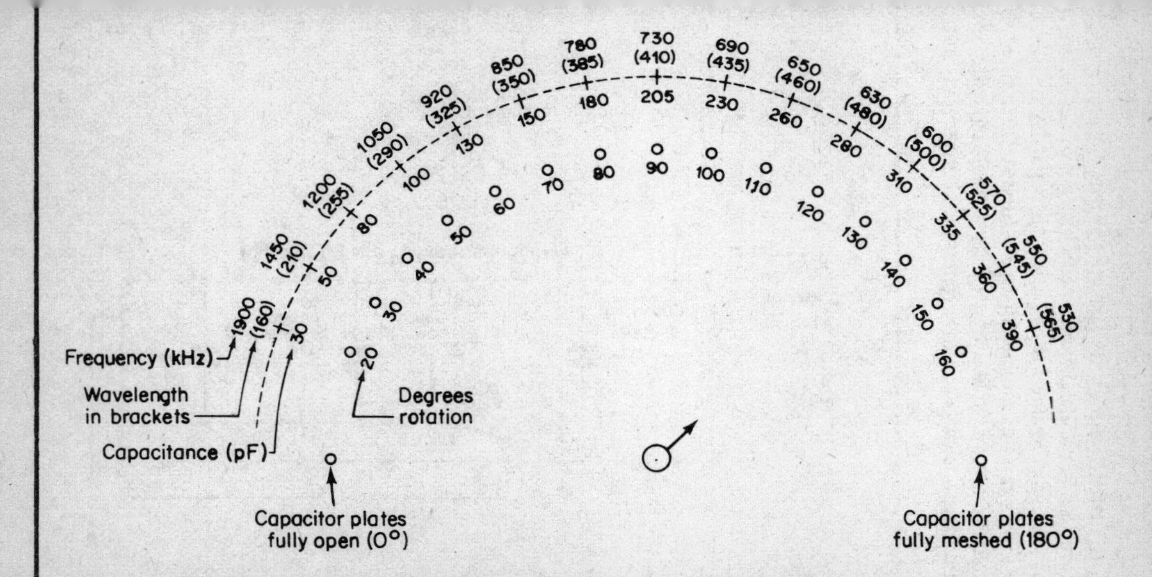

Fig. 18 Approximate capacitance and frequency values for 365 pF variable capacitor and 230 μH coil

5.4 SWITCHED TUNING

This is a feature, simple to provide yet very useful in operation. A switch selects any one of a group of capacitors, each of the correct value for reception of its particular station Fig.19 shows an arrangement for two stations only applied to the circuit of Fig.16. In addition a fully variable capacitor and tuning dial can be switched in if required. The system is not

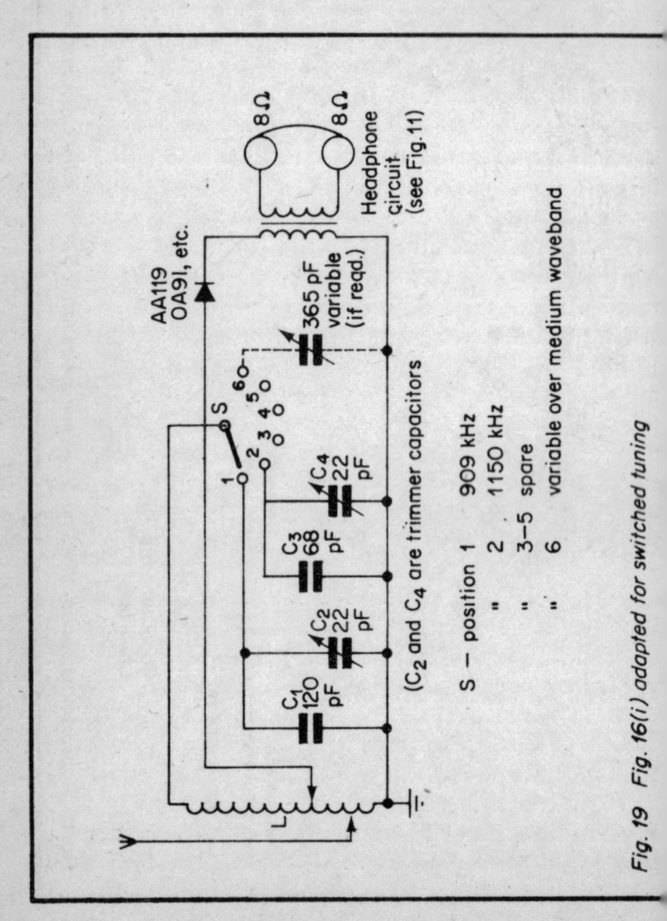

Fig. 19 Fig. 16(i) adapted for switched tuning

expensive and in fact for 2 or 3 fixed stations only, probably costs less than for a single variable. Suppose we are designing for two stations say on 909 and 1150 kHz. We could use a miniature single-pole change-over toggle switch or just two positions of a single-pole 8 or 12-way rotary switch for S. Both cost about the same so the latter might be preferable because it can accommodate more fixed stations if needed later. For the coil of Fig.16 the outer ring of Fig.18 is available for estimating the capacitance required in both cases, for example for 909kHz we might guess 135pF and for 1150kHz, 85pF (note that capacitance and frequency increase in opposite directions round the scale). We have considerable freedom of choice in setting up these two capacitances but a suggestion is to use 22pF *trimmers* with fixed ceramic capacitors as shown for $C_1 - C_4$. Trimmers are tiny variable capacitors, adjusted by a screw. When two capacitors are connected in *parallel* as C_1/C_2 and C_3/C_4 are, the total capacitance is the sum of the individual ones, thus a fixed 120pF in parallel with a 22pF trimmer can be varied over the range just over 120pF (all variable capacitors have some residual capacity) to 120 + 22 = 142pF. Hence 909 kHz can be tuned in by adjusting C_2 to make the combination about 135pF (more accurately, 133pF), this is done by adjusting C_2 until the station is heard at its best. Thereafter whenever S is switched to position 1, the station on 909 kHz should be heard. Similarly for as many other positions on the switch as we wish. Switched tuning and switched selectivity can be used together if required.

Capacitors may have a *maximum working voltage* quoted, above which the component is liable to break down. Any working voltage is suitable for these circuits because all signal voltages are extremely low.

5.5 TWO TUNED CIRCUITS

For many readers who have constructed the basic receiver, good selectivity may still be elusive even with variable tappings on the inductor as in Sections 5.1 and 5.2. Denied as we are in this book of overcoming the problem by the expedient of using transistors and batteries we must continue by exploring other ways of obtaining it. If a single tuned circuit is insufficient, why not use two, one after the other, rather like filtering wine once then a second time to further enhance its

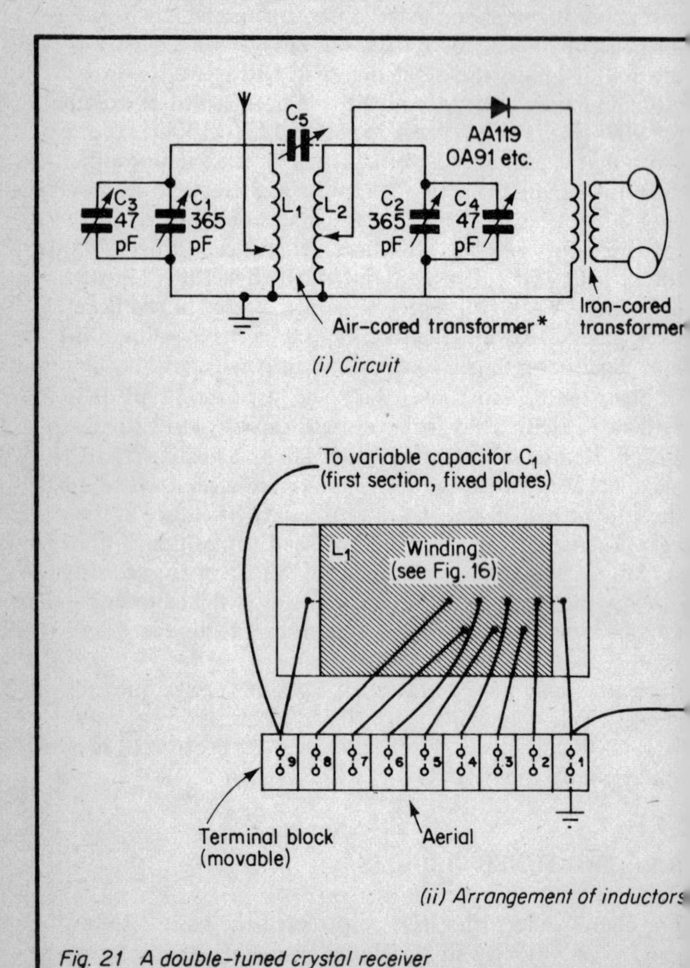

Fig. 21 A double-tuned crystal receiver

clarity? Technically this is a sound idea and the sharpness of tuning increases but one circuit must not damp the other too much for this is the very thing which itself impairs selectivity. Fig.20(i) shows such a circuit. Both inductors are the same as that in Fig.16 but because they are in magnetic contact they

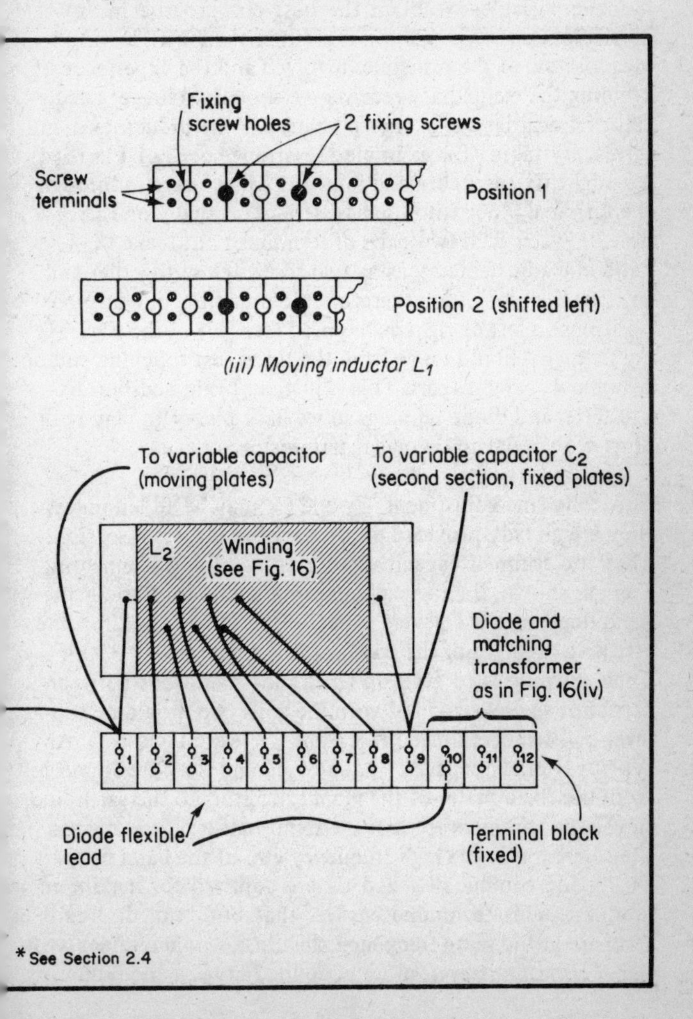

(iii) Moving inductor L_1

* See Section 2.4

form an r.f. transformer as mentioned in Section 2.4. The closer they are to each other, the more energy passes from the aerial to the detector but unfortunately each reduces the sharpness of tuning of the other. The practical circuit therefore requires that the separation between the two inductors is made variable to obtain the best compromise in any particular case. A suggestion is given in Fig.20(ii). Having some idea by now of the principles involved and the experience of building the elementary receiver we should no longer need a full practical layout except perhaps for the inductors themselves. By taking for example the arrangement of Fig.16(ii) we might fix the right-hand inductor by two screws through the terminal block into the base (there is usually one screw hole between each two pairs of terminals) but make the left-hand one adjustable by using two screws close together and shifting the block (and therefore the inductor) one or more positions to left or right as required [see (iii) of the Figure]. Adjustment should range from the tubes just touching end-on to some 4 – 5 cm apart. This adjustment is in addition to the aerial and diode tappings so we have plenty to play with. Start with aerial and diode at terminal 9.

For really fine adjustment, C_3 and C_4 may be added unless they are already provided on the variable capacitor sections. They are trimmer capacitors of small value, by connecting them as shown, their capacitances are added to those of the main ones, thus if C_1 were set at 300pF and C_3 to 20pF the effective capacity of the combination is 300 + 20 = 320pF. Their purpose is to even up (trim) any variations between capacitor sections and between the coils (we should be top-level coil winders indeed if L_1 and L_2 were identical). Any type of trimmer capacitor can be used and they are connected from the fixed plates of the main capacitors to the earth line. In use the trimmers are first set about half-way, a station is then tuned in at the high frequency end of the band by C_1/C_2, finally the trimmers C_3 and C_4 are adjusted for maximum loudness. This technique ensures that both tuned circuits resonate at the same frequency. Just in case when under weak signal conditions even more coupling between the inductors is required than is obtained when they are at their closest, another trimmer capacitor C_5 of maximum value 4.7 or 5.5pF may be added and adjusted as required. Some of the signal then flows directly via C_5 in addition to that through the transformer $L_1 L_2$.

A circuit with double tuning which has already been published twice in this series is still especially worthy of our interest because again we learn more about the principles of radio. From Section 1.8, in looking at the basic idea of detection one could be forgiven for wondering whether blocking off and discarding every alternate half-cycle of the r.f. carrier wave was not somehow inefficient and certainly a power engineer would know it to be. What we have used so far is appropriately known as *half-wave* rectification, there is a more efficient system known as *full-wave*. Let us look at this graphically as in Fig.21(i), from which it is immediately evident that for a given input the full-wave circuit must have a greater output.

The crystal set circuit using full-wave detection is shown in Fig.21(ii), it is basically an adaptation of a standard full-wave rectification circuit used to produce direct current from the alternating current mains. L_1 and L_2 are so wound that when a signal flows in L_3 equal voltages are induced by transformer action in them in such directions that only one of the diodes passes current at a time. When the signal reverses direction the other diode is operative hence full-wave rectification as in (i) is obtained. Winding the coil needs a little more skill than hitherto but the result is a professional looking job as there are no untidy taps, the aerial is controlled by capacitors instead. Details of the coil are at (iii). A 2.5cm (1 inch) diameter tube is required, about 15 cm long. An odd piece of plastic water piping of this outside diameter might be found but failing this the tube can be made from a piece of thin cardboard 15 cm x 8 cm wrapped over a broom handle so that the long edges just meet, and lapped with gummed paper tape. Some 11 gm (less than ½oz) of 0.25mm (SWG 33, AWG 30) enamelled copper wire is required for the three windings and it is essential that L_1 and L_2 are wound in the same direction. The

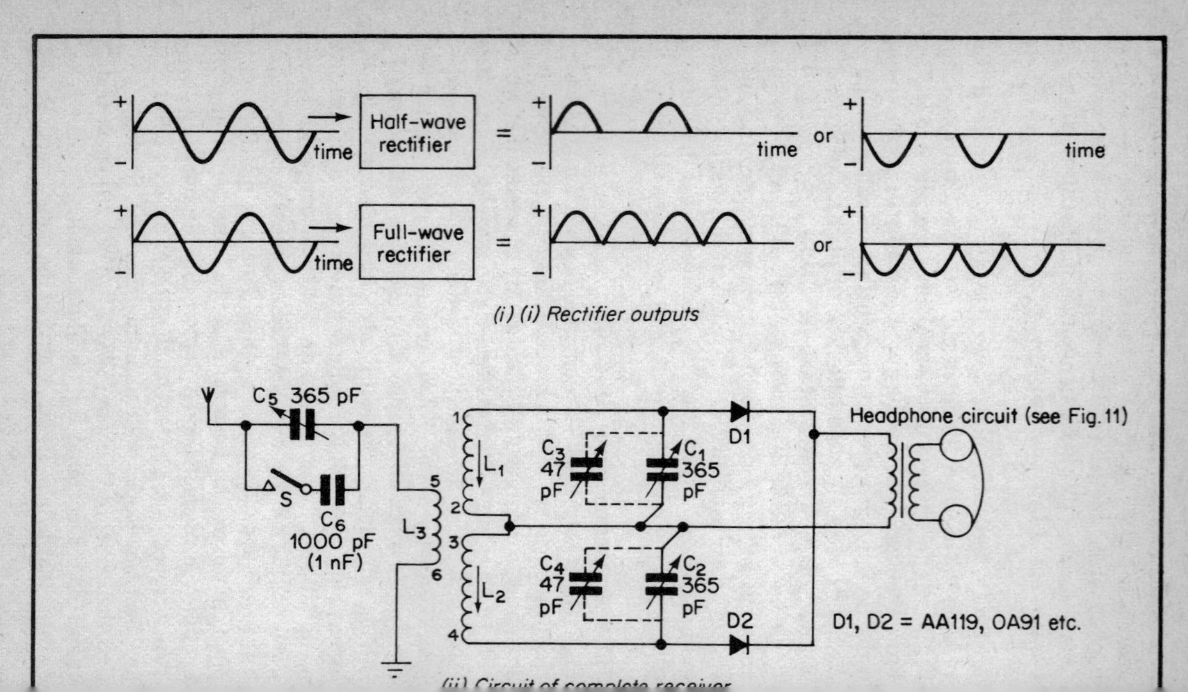

(i) (i) Rectifier outputs

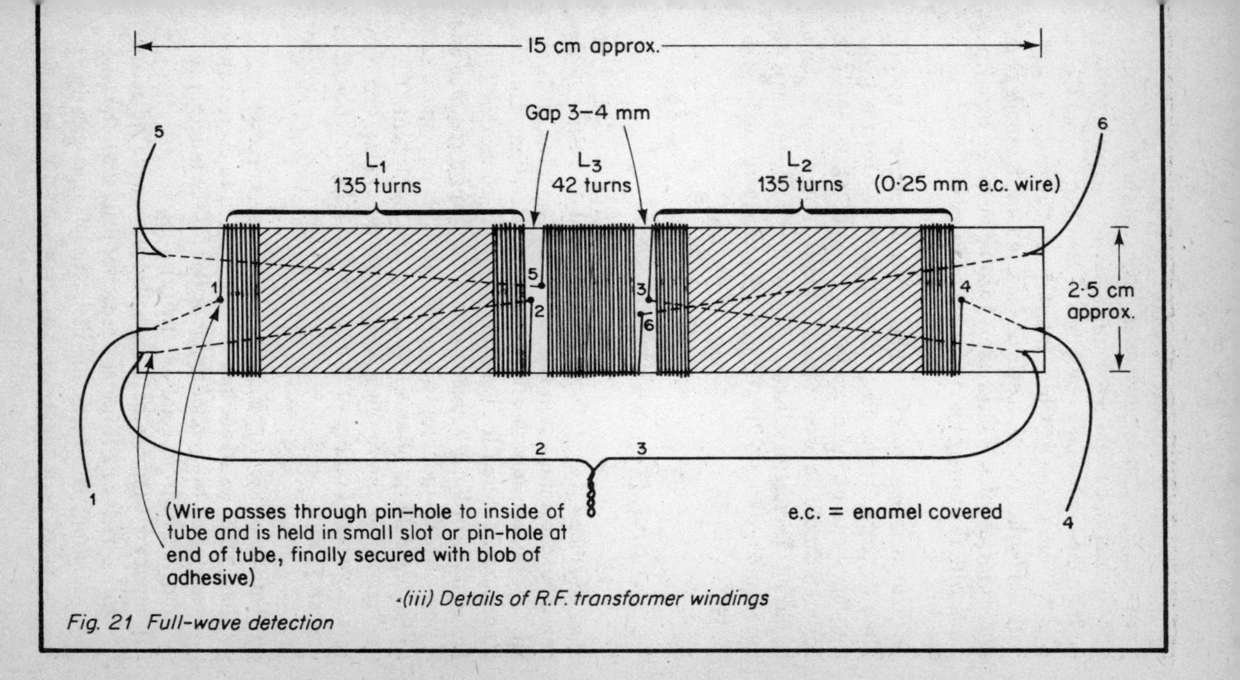

(iii) Details of R.F. transformer windings

Fig. 21 Full-wave detection

complete inductor is not self-supporting, it must therefore be screwed or glued to small wooden blocks on the baseboard. The diodes can be connected either way round but they must both be the same, that is, both marked ends to C_1 and C_2 or equally both to the matching transformer. Capacitor C_5 and switch S (either rotary, toggle or slide, in fact any *single pole, single throw* switch is satisfactory) can be mounted on a front panel with the tuning knob and dial (if fitted).

The trimmer capacitors C_3 and C_4 if added, are set as before. The rule given for the aerial capacitors is that for the high-frequency end of the range (above about 850 kHz, below 350m) S should be open (C_6 disconnected) otherwise S should be closed. Thereafter adjust C_1/C_2 for maximum loudness on the required station followed by C_5 for increased loudness or better selectivity.

5.6 ADDING LONG WAVES

Most broadcast radio transmitters are found on medium waves, hence our main interest in this band. However a few transmit on long waves and therefore need consideration. The inductance required for long waves is many times that for medium, accordingly a greater number of turns is required and if we wound an inductor using the single-layer principle used so far it would be of excessive length and inefficient. The immediate reaction to this is to *layer* or *pile* wind it, that is by successive layers on top of each other. But other inefficiencies now creep in.

(i) with so many turns a smaller gauge wire is necessary, this has higher resistance and such opposition to current flow results in a lower *quality factor* (Q) for the inductor (Q must be high for good selectivity).
(ii) inductor windings have capacitance between adjacent turns, each wire forming a capacitor plate with the wire insulation plus air as the dielectric. This is greatly increased with pile winding because wires not only have

adjacent ones in the same layer but also in the next inner and outer layers. Special winding techniques using machines can minimize this effect but we cannot manage by hand. The net effect of the unwanted capacitance is similar to increasing the winding resistance, hence further lowering the Q.

We have to accept (i) or we end up with an enormous inductor therefore a finer wire is used, for example 0.315mm (SWG 30, AWG 28). For (ii) we can split the winding up to reduce the capacity and reduce it even further by changing to a different type of wire insulation with an extra covering or two of cotton, silk or nylon to increase the wire spacing. Unfortunately such covered wires are not so easily obtainable from the usual component firms and also are rather more expensive. It might be at this stage therefore that we should consider purchasing a ready-made coil. However, for those who wish to persist against all odds, a long wave/medium wave crystal receiver circuit which was published earlier is reproduced here [Fig.22(i)], it uses a home wound inductor for which DSC (double silk covered) or DCC (double cotton covered) wire can probably be obtained from a specialist wire firm. Details of the inductor are in (ii) of the Figure, some 50 – 60 gm (2 oz) of 0.315mm (SWG 30, AWG 28) wire are required and it is again wound on a 4cm diameter, 11cm long cardboard tube (e.g. toilet roll centre). Switch S is for wave band changing, when closed L_1 only is effective and this is the correct inductance with medium waves for a 500pF variable capacitor (using a lower value for C_1 requires an even larger inductor). When S is open, L_2 is added and the inductance rises to that required for long waves (about 2000μH). Note how L_2 is wound in separate piles to reduce the capacity, each pile winding can be built up without side supports but if preferred, cardboard discs can be fitted first [see (iii)] to make the job easier. The aerial and diode tappings are set for a compromise between loudness and selectivity but being a circuit without frills it is unlikely to reject fully local transmitters.

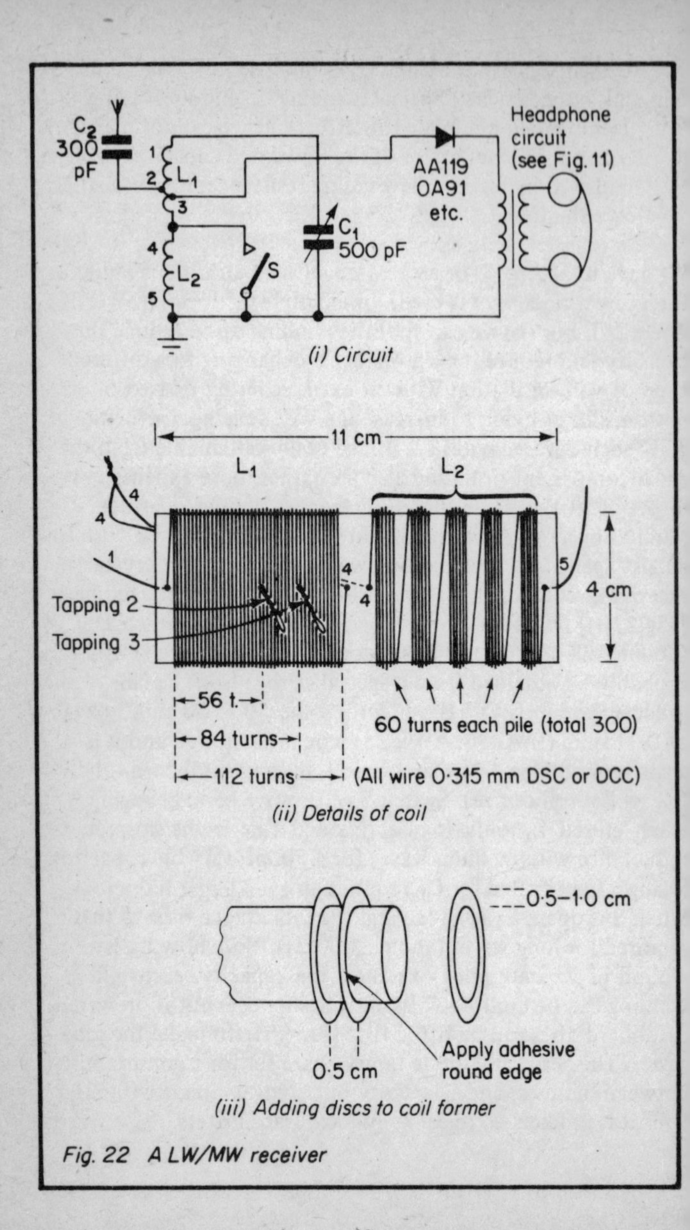

Fig. 22 A LW/MW receiver

.7 USING READY-MADE COILS

n the previous section we begin to get suspicious about the uccess of winding our own coils when selectivity is of major oncern and when this is the case it may well be preferable to urchase ready-made ones instead. These are likely to be more fficient than the home-made types because generally they use netal instead of air cores. By filling the centre of the tube or *ormer* with certain metallic compounds the inductance is aised, thus fewer turns are required so resulting in less vinding resistance and a higher Q which as we have discovered, s the secret of selectivity. Such coils may be available specially for crystal sets or are the aerial coils of a range of ifferent types for home construction of complete transistor eceivers. Diagrams for use are usually included with the coil. Be sure to order for the correct wave range (long or medium) ecause many series of coils include those for short-wave anges also.

Having read so far and perhaps also having built one or more of the designs, our understanding and constructional abilities hould certainly be at the level at which a circuit diagram ncluded with a manufactured coil creates no misgivings.

APPENDIX I
WAVELENGTH – FREQUENCY CONVERSION

LONG WAVEBAND

λ metres	f kHz
1000	300
1050	286
1100	273
1150	261
1200	250
1250	240
1300	231
1350	222
1400	214
1450	207
1500	200
1550	194
1600	188
1650	182
1700	176
1750	171
1800	167
1850	162
1900	158

MEDIUM WAVEBAND

λ metres	f kHz
190	1579
200	1500
210	1429
220	1364
230	1304
240	1250
250	1200
260	1154
270	1111
280	1071
290	1034
300	1000
310	968
320	938
330	909
340	882
350	857
360	833
370	811

λ metres	f kHz
380	789
390	769
400	750
410	732
420	714
430	698
440	682
450	667
460	652
470	638
480	625
490	612
500	600
510	588
520	577
530	566
540	556
550	545

APPENDIX 2
SIMPLIFIED RESONANT CIRCUIT CALCULATIONS

There is a standard, well known formula relating the resonant frequency (f_o) of a tuned circuit with the values of inductance and capacitance therein, it is

$$f_o = \frac{1}{2\pi\sqrt{LC}}$$

where f_o is the resonant frequency in Hz
L is the inductance in henrys
C is the capacitance in farads
π is the ratio of circumference to diameter of a circle and is equal to 3.14159.......

For convenience throughout this book we consider frequency only in kilohertz (f_k), inductance in microhenrys (L_μ) and capacitance in picofarads (C_p), therefore

$$f_o = f_k \times 10^3, \quad L = L_\mu \times 10^{-6}, \quad C = C_p \times 10^{-12}$$

and substituting in the above formula

$$f_k \times 10^3 = \frac{1}{2\pi\sqrt{L\mu \times 10^{-6} \times C_p \times 10^{-12}}}$$

$$= \frac{1}{2\pi \times 10^{-9}\sqrt{L\mu \times C_p}}$$

$$\therefore f_k = \frac{10^{-3} \times 10^9}{2\pi\sqrt{L\mu C_p}} = \frac{10^6}{2\pi\sqrt{L\mu C_p}}$$

$$\therefore f_k^2 = \frac{10^{12}}{4\pi^2 L\mu C_p} = \frac{2533 \times 10^7}{L\mu C_p}$$

giving us three useful formulae:

$$L_\mu = \frac{2533 \times 10^7}{f_k^2 C_p},$$

$$C_p = \frac{2533 \times 10^7}{f_k^2 L_\mu},$$

$$f_k = \sqrt{\frac{2533 \times 10^7}{L_\mu C_p}}.$$

With scientific calculators there is little difficulty because scientific notation is available but with a home or pocket calculator which has no such facility and displays only 8 digits, it is still straightforward as long as it has a $\sqrt{x}$ facility.

We cannot get 2533 followed by 7 0's into the display hence work with 4 and multiply by 1000 later. As an example, when $L_\mu = 230$ and $C_p = 365$

$$f_k = \sqrt{\frac{25330000}{230 \times 365} \times 1000} = \sqrt{301.72722 \times 1000}$$

$$= \sqrt{301727.22} = 549.3 \text{ (kHz)}.$$

Similarly for an inductor of 2600μH, the capacitance required to tune to 210 kHz is

$$C_p = \frac{25330000}{210 \times 210 \times 2600} \times 1000 = 220.9 \text{ (pF)}.$$

APPENDIX 3
SOLDERING

To be accomplished at soldering is an asset indeed for so many jobs around the home can be undertaken once the techniques and principles are understood, even plumbing. But that is another story, we are concerned with electrical joints only and happily success with these is really quite easy to achieve.

A3.1 SOLDER

As we see in Section 1.4, electrons flow easily within a conductor it is therefore imperative that should the latter be connected or jointed to another conductor, tag or terminal, the joint itself should not resist this flow. This is accomplished by the two metals being in such intimate contact that electrons flow across the joint as though the metal were continuous. A screw connection such as used in the terminal block of Fig.14 achieves this by the screw being forced into the metal to give a very tight and clean contact. Soldering is another method of joining two conductors together and it provides an excellent and secure electrical contact. Electrical solder is an alloy of tin and lead usually in a 60/40 ratio, this melts and flows at 190°C. Water boils at 100°C so as far as we personally are concerned, molten solder and soldering irons must be treated with respect and fingers kept off. Tin is a metal which readily alloys with copper, that is, it actually mixes with the copper at its surface, thus solder joining two pieces of copper acts as a cement and because of its intimate contact with the surface, electrons flow across without hindrance. Electrical solder is called *soft*, naturally it has some of the characteristic softness of lead, in fact wires can be peeled out of a soldered joint. *Hard* solder on the other hand has a higher melting point and results in a much stronger joint but it is more difficult to manipulate.

It is easy to realize that for solder to form an alloy with copper the surface of the latter must be immaculate, that is with absolutely no dirt, corrosion or *oxide* in the way. Copper readily forms its oxide when it is heated. The oxide is not copper although it is derived from it and therefore any present must be removed. Once copper is coated with solder, formation of oxide is prevented, the process is aptly called *tinning*.

Solder flowing over clean metal and forming an alloy correctly is like water flowing, it has the resemblance of *wetness*, conversely if it tries to flow over a contaminated surface with which it cannot alloy it does not give the appearance of wetting the metal. To assist in prevention of oxide and to aid in cleanliness a *flux* (= to make flow) is employed and to make our life easier modern solders are available looking rather like a thick, soft grey wire with a resin flux running down the centre. For us a solder about 0.7mm diameter (SWG 22, AWG 21) is most suitable. It is available in small coils or larger reels.

A3.2 SOLDERING TOOLS

Undoubtedly the most useful and most used type of soldering "iron" (the working part is actually copper) is the electric one, a heating element within the barrel of the iron heats one end of a copper *bit*, heat travels along the bit to the working end to set up a temperature above the melting point of solder so that solder in contact with the bit melts. A 20 or 25 watt iron has a bit small enough for fine electrical work but it cannot handle bigger jobs which extract heat from the bit faster than the element generates it. A non-electric iron has a copper bit on an iron rod with a handle at the end remote from the bit, the bit is heated separately, for example in a gas flame, when the bit has cooled it must be reheated.

The two almost essential tools for wiring are (i) a pair of long-nosed pliers, with a little practice fine wires can be manipulated quite easily, and (ii) a pair of wire or side-cutters. These two items may seem expensive for in fact they may cost more than the whole crystal set (excluding headphones) but they have many uses around the home so if the family toolbox does not already possess them, the cost will soon be repaid. However it is just possible to manage without them, whether to purchase depends so much on what future intentions are with regard to electronics as a hobby. A small file will also be occasionally required for re-shaping the iron bit.

A3.3 SOLDERING

For a soldered joint, not only the parts to be joined but also the tip of the soldering iron must be tinned. Assuming an electric iron, plug in and after a few minutes it will have reached working temperature. Do not rest the bit on anything metal otherwise heat is conducted away. Most small irons have a hook attached so that they can be hung in an upright position with the bit uppermost. Wipe across the tip of the iron with a small piece of clean rag, if the tip surface is silvery bright it is suitably tinned, failing this, unplug and allow to cool then file until clean copper is exposed all over the tip, then apply the end of a piece of cored solder. When the solder has received sufficient heat from the iron it will melt and flow over the tip, forming a bead of molten solder. If this is wiped away the tip will appear bright and tinned. Remember that little beads of molten solder can raise larger blisters! Filing and re-tinning the tip is only needed occasionally when it has become pitted.

Most component wires and tags are tinned for us during manufacture but if they are dirty or corroded, re-tinning may be necessary. However for practice let us tin and then joint two pieces of copper wire (if no untinned wire is available then tinning can be removed with emery cloth). Wire insulation can first be removed where necessary by cutting round with a knife (carefully, so as not to cut the wire itself) and pulling off. The ends of the wire must be bright copper by rubbing with sandpaper, emery cloth or by scraping. For solder to flow over the surface the wire temperature must be above that of the melting point of solder. Firstly add a little solder to the tip of the iron as shown in Fig.23(i), next push the end of the wire into the bead to heat the wire (ii), then feed solder (and flux) onto the wire and molten bead, it will flow over the copper and in fact the solder can be "painted" on (iii). Then move the iron and solder along the wire slowly continuing the painting process as far as is required (some surplus solder may fall off, this is inevitable when we start). Finally remove the wire and immediately wipe with the clean rag for a bright, silvery surface to appear, only the surplus solder wipes off, not the alloy.

Tin two pieces of wire and then twist the tinned ends together for about 1cm. Apply solder to the twist as we did in (iii) for the single wire and it will flow easily into the joint, cementing the two wires together, they can subsequently be untwisted only with considerable difficulty by tearing out of the solder.

Fig.23(iv) illustrates the soldering of a capacitor lead to a tag (for clarity we assume that the tag is already connected to something). First check that all surfaces are tinned then loop the capacitor wire through the tag. Press the tip of the iron against the tag and feed solder between the tag and the tip as shown. As the joint heats up the solder will flow, sufficient being fed in to ensure that the wire is fully cemented to the tag. Remove the iron. It looks as though we need three hands for iron, solder and capacitor so the latter must be made self-supporting, perhaps by squeezing the loop of wire onto the tag. Once soldered it certainly must not be moved until the solder has set, quite a short time, especially if we blow on the joint to cool it. Later on when a little skill has developed it will be found possible to solder wires without making a loop through the tag, this is especially useful for experimental work because it facilitates later removal of components.

Provided that all parts are brightly tinned and solder is seen to flow easily into all the crevices and not form globules which

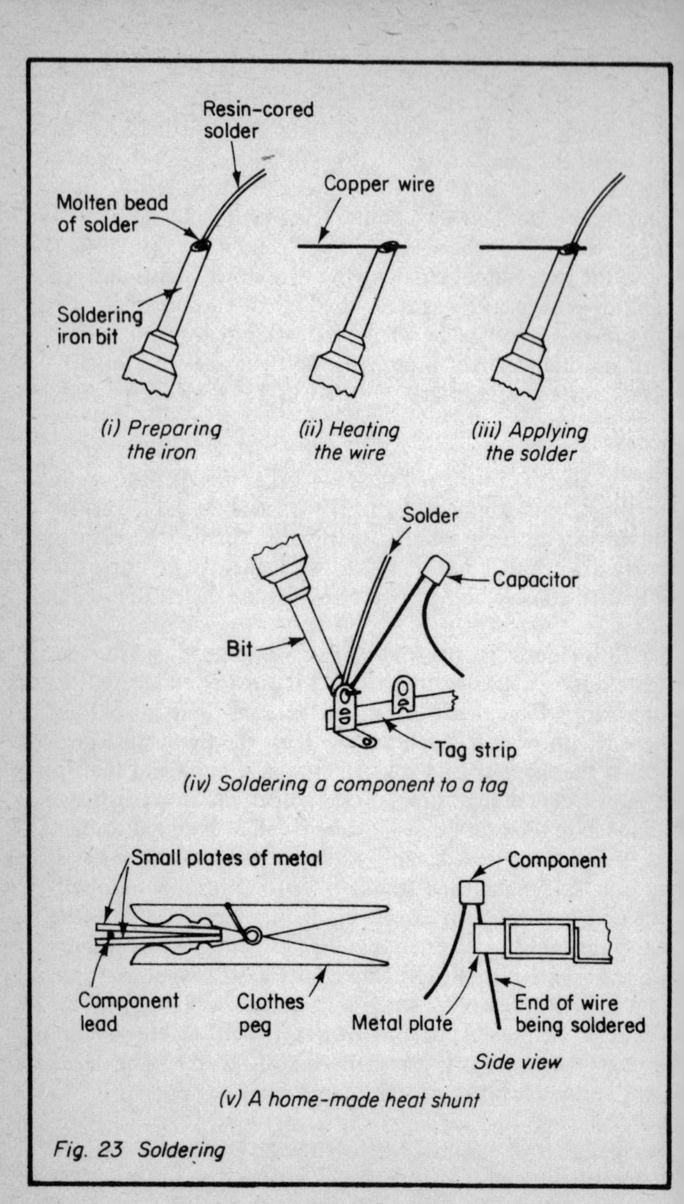
Resin-cored solder
Molten bead of solder
Soldering iron bit
Copper wire
(i) Preparing the iron
(ii) Heating the wire
(iii) Applying the solder
Solder
Capacitor
Bit
Tag strip
(iv) Soldering a component to a tag
Small plates of metal
Component lead
Clothes peg
Component
Metal plate
End of wire being soldered
Side view
(v) A home-made heat shunt
Fig. 23 Soldering

refuse to flow, a perfect joint is obtained. *Dry* joints occur when dirt or oxide or perhaps too much flux prevent the solder from alloying – a little experience will take care of this.

Finally, remember that if used carelessly a soldering iron and molten solder can cause burns. Also even when unplugged the bit may still remain hot for sometime.

A3.4 HEAT SHUNTS

Some components, especially diodes and transistors are damaged by excessive heat arriving along their connecting wires. Thus soldering operations should not be prolonged nor should the leads be shortened. A further protection is provided by the use of a *heat shunt*, just a small chunk of metal clipped to the lead near the body of the component. Heat flowing along the lead is absorbed by the shunt and is therefore prevented from continuing its passage along the wire into the heart of the device. Heat shunts can be purchased quite cheaply or made for example by clipping strips of metal (copper, aluminium etc) onto the wire using a clothes peg [see Fig.23(v)].

A long appendix because it is easier to solder than to explain how to do it. Good luck!

PUBLISHER'S NOTE

Readers who feel they would like, or have a need to understand electronics more fully may be interested in a series of books by the same author entitled "Elements of Electronics". The series starts at the very beginning and assumes that the reader has no mathematical experience whatsoever and therefore teaches all that is required as each book progresses. It is an educational step-by-step series in which the reader can advance his or her knowledge book by book. The publication numbers are BP62, 63, 64, 77 and 89 and full details are contained within the current Catalogue of Babani Books.

Please note overleaf is a list of other titles that are available in our range of Radio, Electronics and Computer Books.

These should be available from all good Booksellers, Radio Component Dealers and Mail Order Companies.

However, should you experience difficulty in obtaining any title in your area, then please write directly to the publisher enclosing payment to cover the cost of the book plus adequate postage.

If you would like a complete catalogue of our entire range of Radio, Electronics and Computer Books then please send a Stamped Addressed Envelope to:

BERNARD BABANI (publishing) LTD
THE GRAMPIANS
SHEPHERDS BUSH ROAD
LONDON W6 7NF
ENGLAND

160	Coil Design and Construction Manual	1.50p
202	Handbook of Integrated Circuits (IC's) Equivalents & Substitutes	1.75p
205	First Book of Hi-Fi Loudspeaker Enclosures	95p
221	28 Tested Transistor Projects	1.25p
222	Solid State Short Wave Receivers for Beginners	1.25p
223	50 Projects Using IC CA3130	1.25p
224	50 CMOS IC Projects	1.25p
225	A Practical Introduction to Digital IC's	1.25p
226	How to Build Advanced Short Wave Receivers	1.20p
227	Beginners Guide to Building Electronic Projects	1.50p
228	Essential Theory for the Electronics Hobbyist	1.25p
RCC	Resistor Colour Code Disc	20p
BP1	First Book of Transistor Equivalents and Substitutes	95p
BP2	Handbook of Radio, TV & Ind. & Transmitting Tube & Valve Equiv.	60p
BP6	Engineers and Machinists Reference Tables	75p
BP7	Radio and Electronic Colour Codes and Data Chart	40p
BP14	Second Book of Transistor Equivalents and Substitutes	1.75p
BP24	52 Projects Using IC741	1.25p
BP27	Chart of Radio Electronic Semiconductor and Logic Symbols	50p
BP32	How to Build Your Own Metal and Treasure Locators	1.75p
BP33	Electronic Calculator Users Handbook	1.50p
BP34	Practical Repair and Renovation of Colour TVs	1.25p
BP35	Handbook of IC Audio Preamplifier & Power Amplifier Construction	1.75p
BP36	50 Circuits Using Germanium, Silicon and Zener Diodes	95p
BP37	50 Projects Using Relays, SCR's and TRIACs	1.75p
BP39	50 (FET) Field Effect Transistor Projects	1.75p
BP40	Digital IC Equivalents and Pin Connections	2.50p
BP41	Linear IC Equivalents and Pin Connections	3.75p
BP42	50 Simple L.E.D. Circuits	95p
BP43	How to Make Walkie-Talkies	1.50p
BP44	IC555 Projects	1.95p
BP45	Projects in Opto-Electronics	1.75p
BP46	Radio Circuits Using IC's	1.35p
BP47	Mobile Discotheque Handbook	1.35p
BP48	Electronic Projects for Beginners	1.35p
BP49	Popular Electronic Projects	1.45p
BP50	IC LM3900 Projects	1.35p
BP51	Electronic Music and Creative Tape Recording	1.75p
BP52	Long Distance Television Reception (TV–DX) for the Enthusiast	1.95p
BP53	Practical Electronic Calculations and Formulae	2.95p
BP55	Radio Stations Guide	1.75p
BP56	Electronic Security Devices	1.75p
BP57	How to Build Your Own Solid State Oscilloscope	1.50p
BP58	50 Circuits Using 7400 Series IC's	1.50p
BP59	Second Book of CMOS IC Projects	1.50p
BP60	Practical Construction of Pre-amps, Tone Controls, Filters & Attn	1.45p
BP61	Beginners Guide to Digital Techniques	95p
BP62	Elements of Electronics – Book 1	2.25p
BP63	Elements of Electronics – Book 2	2.25p
BP64	Elements of Electronics – Book 3	2.25p
BP65	Single IC Projects	1.50p
BP66	Beginners Guide to Microprocessors and Computing	1.75p
BP67	Counter Driver and Numeral Display Projects	1.75p
BP68	Choosing and Using Your Hi-Fi	1.65p
BP69	Electronic Games	1.75p
BP70	Transistor Radio Fault-Finding Chart	50p
BP71	Electronic Household Projects	1.75p
BP72	A Microprocessor Primer	1.75p
BP73	Remote Control Projects	1.95p
BP74	Electronic Music Projects	1.75p
BP75	Electronic Test Equipment Construction	1.75p
BP76	Power Supply Projects	1.75p
BP77	Elements of Electronics – Book 4	2.95p
BP78	Practical Computer Experiments	1.75p
BP79	Radio Control for Beginners	1.75p
BP80	Popular Electronic Circuits – Book 1	1.95p
BP81	Electronic Synthesiser Projects	1.75p
BP82	Electronic Projects Using Solar-Cells	1.95p
BP83	VMOS Projects	1.95p
BP84	Digital IC Projects	1.95p
BP85	International Transistor Equivalents Guide	2.95p
BP86	An Introduction to Basic Programming Techniques	1.95p
BP87	Simple L.E.D. Circuits – Book 2	1.35p
BP88	How to Use Op-Amps	2.25p
BP89	Elements of Electronics – Book 5	2.95p
BP90	Audio Projects	1.95p
BP91	An Introduction to Radio DX-ing	1.95p
BP92	Electronics Simplified – Crystal Set Construction	1.95p
BP93	Electronic Timer Projects	1.95p
BP94	Electronic Projects for Cars and Boats	1.95p
BP95	Model Railway Projects	1.95p
BP96	C B Projects	1.95p
BP97	IC Projects for Beginners	1.95p
BP98	Popular Electronic Circuits – Book 2	2.25p
BP99	Mini-Matrix Board Projects	1.95p
BP100	An Introduction to Video	1.95p
BP101	How to Identify Unmarked IC's	65p
BP102	The 6809 Companion	1.95p
BP103	Multi-Circuit Board Projects	1.95p
BP104	Electronic Science Projects	2.25p
BP105	Aerial Projects	1.95p
BP106	Modern Op-Amp Projects	1.95p